CURIOSITIES
of BIRD LIFE

**By J.D. Macdonald, Derek Goodwin
and Helmut E. Adler**

CASTLE BOOKS, INC.   New York
Distributed by BOOK SALES, Inc. 352 Park Avenue South, New York 10

PICTURE CREDITS

The publishers wish to thank the following people and organizations for use of photographs in this book:

American Museum of Natural History; Australian News and Information Bureau; British Columbia Government; C. G. Fairchild; L. A. Fuertes; Derek Goodwin; J. Malcolm Greany; C. J. Henry; W. F. Kubichek; Frank W. Lane; J. D. Macdonald; Michigan Conservation Department; New Zealand National Publicity Studios; Provincial Museum, Victoria, B. C.; Hermann Schunemann; Texas Game and Fish Commission; Ronald Thompson; U. S. Fish and Wildlife Service; Zoological Society of London.

1967 Printing

Bird Behavior
Copyright © 1962
by STERLING PUBLISHING CO., INC.
419 Park Avenue South, New York, N. Y., 10016

Published by special arrangement with Museum Press, Ltd., London, whose
"Bird Biology" © 1959, J. D. Macdonald and
"Bird Behaviour" © 1961, Derek Goodwin,
furnished the basic text for Parts I and II of this volume

CONTENTS

Preface

THE TREND of our times is for people to move into the cities and suburbs. Yet many of us feel the loss of contact with nature that this move inevitably has brought about. Statistics show the ever-increasing popularity of keeping dogs or cats, or raising tropical fish in the home. Many of us, who cannot devote the time or do not have the space for such activities can at least look with understanding and interest at such animal life as may come our way.

Birds are ideal objects for such study. Some species, such as the feral pigeon and the starling, have taken up city life themselves. Many more have found suburban life to their liking. On vacation or in parks and along beaches we can spot many more birds carrying on their conspicuous activities. Because of their high visibility, their pleasant song, and their capacity to become quite tame, birds have become the favorites of many people starved for a contact with nature. That this is so, is no surprise. Accessible mammals tend to be nocturnal and secretive, or a nuisance, such as rats and mice. There are many more insects than birds, but somehow I doubt if "insect watching" will ever supplant bird watching as a hobby, although we may occasionally watch a fly or mosquito quite closely, before

Pair of barn swallows at rest with young. The barn swallow was originally a cave nester but now it usually nests in barns and other buildings. It is found widely both in America and the Old World.

exterminating it. There is, however, little pleasure felt in doing so!

Bird watching traditionally concerns itself with the identification of as many species as possible. As a hobby it has a built-in limitation. Sooner or later all common species will have been identified. An increasing number of people want to know more about the bird's world, and to them the nature of the contents of an egg is just as important as the features that distinguish a song sparrow from an English sparrow.

The purpose of this book is to introduce the beginner to the main features of the life of birds. There are many excellent texts on ornithology, the science of birds, and many technical journals in which the studies of scientists from all over the world are reported. This book aims to report their findings in everyday language, avoiding the jargon in which scientific concepts are so often couched. It is nevertheless completely reliable from the point of view of ornithology and the study of animal behavior.

J. D. Macdonald, the head of the bird department in the British Museum (Natural History), in London, is responsible for Chapters I through X, the parts of the book dealing with the anatomy, physiology, and also some of the ecology of birds. Derek Goodwin, who wrote Chapters XI through XVII, dealing with bird behavior, also works in the British Museum. He has wide experience in observing their behavior, including a period in the pigeon service with the British forces in the Middle East during World War II.

Bird behavior knows no national boundaries. As editor, I have made some changes in the interest of the American reader, substituting American terms for some species which are known to us under a different name, and familiar birds for unfamiliar British species, where this could be done. On the main the content did not have to be changed much from the British text, since the authors had chosen their examples from many birds the world over. Nothing, of course, was changed where the authors give us the priceless benefit of their personal experience. The editor assumes responsibility for any changes which actually were made.

Chapters XVIII and XIX on migration, and orientation, navigation and homing, have been contributed by the editor. His work in the Department of Animal Behavior, at the American Museum of Natural History in New York, has long been concerned with the cues which birds might use for orientation and navigation. As a comparative psychologist (he is Associate Professor of Psychology at Yeshiva University in New York), his interest is particularly focused on finding out the why and the how of behavior. The word "instinct," which has so often been used as a term of explanation for this behavior, will on closer examination be seen as nothing but another way of saying that we cannot, as yet, explain something.

HELMUT E. ADLER

Jamaica, N.Y.
June 1962.

6

Section 1

CHAPTER I

Nest and Eggs

THE LIFE of a bird starts as an egg, laid into a nest, so it seems right to start an account of bird behavior with this important event in its life history. Much care has gone into the selection of nest site and territory, before the parent birds are satisfied and at the proper time have come into breeding condition. In many of the lower animals, reptiles for instance, mating is more or less the final event of the breeding season; as often as not males have no further interest in what takes place, nor have many of the females either after the eggs are laid. But in birds, with the exception of the cuckoo and other parasitic species, and members of the mound bird family of the Australian Region (see Fig. 4) which leave their eggs to be incubated in hot sand or rotting vegetation, successful reproduction requires that mating should be accompanied by a number of other events, like nest building, parental incubation of eggs and the protection and education of the young. Although some birds begin nest building, especially those whose nests are rather elaborate, before mating takes place— sometimes it is part of the courtship behavior —completion of the building is usually dependent on successful mating, and I will refer to it here in that sequence.

NESTS

It is interesting that in many species with territorial habits the territory is selected before the nest is built, and yet it is important that a suitable nest site should be available: the house should be on the property, so to speak. Occasionally a hen will build outside the selected area, and this puts the cock to some trouble to extend his jurisdiction to include it. For various reasons, protection mainly, some birds require rather special sites, and if none is available they will not occupy that area. But usually food is the limiting factor, and if a bird can satisfy its special needs or if it has a wide range of tastes it will build in a variety of places. In locating nests there are two main protective measures: inaccessibility and camouflage. Judged by our standards, which are of little concern to most birds, it is easy to find crows' nests, but they are high up in trees and difficult to reach, whereas the nests of a bird like the meadowlark are on the ground and easily reached—if you can find them. If the crow built its present type of nest on the ground I feel sure there would soon be many fewer crows.

Nest sites and nest construction are as varied as the birds themselves. There are

7

few places on land which some bird does not make use of, and even open water where there is floating vegetation is used by the grebes for their raft-like nests. Incidentally, the ability to find a bird's nest appears to be an art for which some people have a natural flair—I have a sister who could beat me any day—but, on the whole, success comes with practice and some inside knowledge of where to look and what to look for.

Young goshawks. The nest is a large flat-topped structure of sticks and twigs placed in a tree. This type of nest is built by most hawks and related birds of prey. These young are about two-thirds grown and their nestling down is being replaced by true feathers.

EGGS

Eggs are a very important part of the life of birds. They are as important as the chicks which come out of them when they are incubated. I say this because I wish to emphasize that nobody should take an egg from a nest of a wild bird who would not also take a live chick. Most of us would think twice before doing that. The few who do take eggs and chicks after thinking twice are usually people engaged in scientific studies directed towards a better understanding of birds, a knowledge which is sometimes to the ultimate benefit of the birds themselves. Please, therefore, if you are a young naturalist beginning a study of birds do not take eggs from nests thinking that they matter little or that they are dead things. You will not be a true naturalist if you are merely interested in having eggs in a box because they are pretty objects.

Rate of egg-laying

There is a special feature connected with egg-laying. I wonder if you have noticed it. The clue is egg-laying in birds compared with egg-laying in other animals. You may have observed, or noted in your reading, that frogs, fish and turtles, for example, deposit their eggs all at once, or at least in large batches. All the eggs are in the body of the female, like a litter of kittens in a pregnant cat, ready to be born at the same time. No bird lays its usual clutch of eggs in this way, at least clutches of more than one egg. The eggs are laid one at a time at intervals of up to a day or longer. I expect you know that it is normally impossible to get more than one egg per day from a domestic hen, although breeds have been developed which are little more than egg-laying machines.

The reason for this spaced egg-laying becomes clear when you remember that because birds fly, their weight is of vital importance. The construction of birds, like the design of flying machines, is directed mainly toward reduction in weight without

Kiwi and its eggs. The kiwi, a flightless New Zealand bird of nocturnal habits, lays an extraordinarily large egg for its size.

loss of efficiency. A clutch of unlaid eggs would increase the weight of the bird to such an extent that it would be unable to fly, or at least be greatly restricted in its movements in the air. Eggs of the great blue heron, for example, would increase the bird's weight by about 20 per cent, a buzzard would increase by about 25 per cent, coot 40 per cent, pheasant 50 per cent, mallard 60 per cent, red-headed woodpecker 75 per cent, black-capped chickadee 100 per cent and the tiny golden-crowned kinglet 120 per cent.

Structure of an egg

What does an egg consist of? We all know what it looks like: an object with a hard shell containing some glutinous fluid and a yellowish core. The yellow core or yolk is a single body cell of the kind essential in reproduction. It began in the hen's reproductive organs, the ovary, when these were stimulated into activity in the breeding season. At its beginning it was no bigger than any other body cell (and they are usually microscopic in size), but food material or yolk was packed into it, like air into a balloon. When the yolk-filled cell, now called ovum, had its required amount of yolk it was released from the ovary and caught in the funnel-shaped upper end of the oviduct.

The ovum is not just a dead sackful of yolk. It is very much alive, for it has a minute spot, the cicatricle or germ plasm, which is contained in all living ova. In reproduction these elements are activated by union with one of the many sperm cells passed into the hen's oviduct during copulation. This union of cells, or fertilization, usually takes place at the upper end of the oviduct, and thereafter the egg continues on its way down the long tube where it is invested with various materials secreted by glands in the oviduct walls. First to be added is a thick layer of albumen or egg-white, which is clear and glutinous.

The yolk is suspended in the middle of this and you may wonder why it does not fall to the bottom. It is supported in this way: the first layer of albumen is much tougher than the rest and it is wrapped around the yolk and the ends twisted, like the ends of a candy wrapper, and then extended toward the poles of the egg where it becomes

Fig. 1. Anatomy of an egg. The portion enclosed by the vitelline membrane is a single cell which developed in the ovary. The surrounding structures were added in the oviduct.

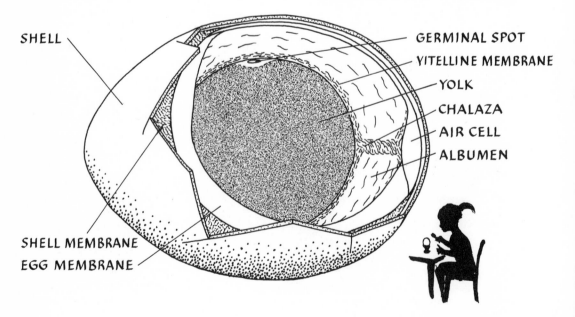

SHELL

GERMINAL SPOT

VITELLINE MEMBRANE

YOLK

CHALAZA

AIR CELL

ALBUMEN

SHELL MEMBRANE

EGG MEMBRANE

anchored. The twists are called chalaza and you may have seen them in an egg, raw or boiled, and wondered what they are. When the deposition of albumen is complete it is covered with a fairly tough egg membrane. The shell structures are next laid down; first there is a shell membrane, which is separate from the egg membrane, and on this the limy shell is built by the shell glands in the end portion of the oviduct. The final touch to this "architectural marvel," as it has been described, is the addition to the eggshells of many species of various pigments in many pleasing colors and designs. The shell is not solid, but is riddled with numerous tiny pores.

Color, size and shape

I expect you know that eggs vary a lot in color, shape and size from one species to another. You may not be so well acquainted with the fact that sometimes there is a big range of color variation in the eggs of one species. In the murre, for instance, the eggs may be uniformly colored, white or creamy or brownish or bluish, or they may be lightly or heavily mottled with blotches and streaks of various kinds. But, on the whole, colors and markings are fairly constant for each species. Eggs can be divided into two main color groups, those which are white and those which are colored in some way. White or off-white or very pale eggs are typical of many birds, as for example, pigeons, owls, woodpeckers, the cormorant or shag, swift, kingfisher, and wren. You will notice that many of these are types of birds which nest in holes or have domed nests or put their nests in places not easily reached; or always cover the eggs, as pigeons do, unless the sitting bird is surprised off the nest, so that they are never exposed to the sight of egg-eating predators.

In eggs which are naturally hidden away out of the sight or reach of predators, color is of little importance as regards protection, but in eggs which are left exposed in places easily found, as on the ground, it is important that they should be inconspicuous. Thus the eggs of many ground-nesting birds blend in color with their immediate surroundings; they are well camouflaged or cryptic (colored to be inconspicuous). What is of special interest, the mothers avoid drawing attention to them by not having a well-defined nest. The eggs of birds like the oyster catcher, whimbrel, ringed plover and common tern, although strongly marked when you see them in your hand, fit in so perfectly with their environment that if you take your eyes off them for a moment you have to concentrate your attention to locate them again. The eggs often lie in what is only a slight depression, having little resemblance to what we usually think of as a nest.

But the eggs of all ground-nesting birds are not cryptic, even sometimes in cases where nests are very exposed. In these instances it is the birds themselves which are very difficult to see when sitting. Whip-poor-will, woodcock and pheasant (hen of course) belong to this category. These birds sit very close when danger is near and only desert the nest at the last possible moment; their eggs are not well camouflaged. Terns and other conspicuous ground nesters usually slip away from their eggs at the first sign of danger. Possibly the ideal protective arrangement would be for both birds and eggs to be camouflaged, and this condition is nearly achieved in the ptarmigan. I have stroked sitting birds, after much difficulty in finding them, and when they have gently been persuaded to leave the nest, the eggs are found to be quite inconspicuous.

These are examples of egg color in relation to the places in which the eggs are laid ready to be incubated. But one has to mention one additional and very special example. It is variation in the eggs of the cuckoo in relation to the eggs of the birds in whose nests cuckoos put their eggs. I am sure you know that the cuckoo is parasitic; it does not rear its own family but deposits its eggs in the nests of other birds. (However, unlike its European cousin, the native black-billed cuckoo usually builds a nest and rears its own young. When it does lay its eggs into another bird's nest, the species chiefly parasitized are the

(Above) The woodcock's nest consists of a slight depression among dead leaves and other debris on the ground in woodland. The eggs, although spotted, are not as well camouflaged as those of many other ground-nesting birds.

(Left) The woodcock's eggs are, however, protected by the incubating parent who sits very closely and whose cryptic plumage with its beautiful and intricate markings of brown, gray, black and chestnut blend with the background and make the sitting bird very hard to pick out.

chipping sparrow, yellow warbler, catbird and wood thrush.) Usually only one egg is deposited in the nest of each host and the interesting point is that eggs are variable in color. There is a marked tendency for the cuckoo eggs to get to look like those of the host species. This usually happens when a "strain" of cuckoos parasitize the same species, when, for example, a cuckoo born in a pipit's nest in turn deposits its egg in a nest of the same species, and so on from one generation to another. Incidentally, in an African finch-like bird which parasitizes a certain warbler the process has gone a bit further, for the chicks of the parasite look exactly like the chicks of the host, although the adults of both species are quite different.

There is an interesting point in connection with the size of cuckoo eggs. They are relatively small, much smaller than eggs of other species of similar body size. A cuckoo is about the same weight, for example, as blackbird and robin, less than 100 grams (gm.), but its egg is only about 3 gm.

whereas the eggs of the others are about 7 to 9 gm. This reduction in size, as with color variation, seems to be an adaptation to match the size of the eggs of the species parasitized, for these are usually birds smaller than the cuckoo. A general rule about egg size or egg weight is that although larger birds lay larger eggs the egg size does not increase in the same proportion as the birds do; in other words a bird twice the size of another usually has an egg less than twice the size.

Egg shapes are not all like the egg of the domestic hen, which is described as oval, and which as you know is thicker and blunter at one end and thinner and sharper at the other. Egg shapes are named and classified in various ways. Eggs which are blunter at one end than the hen's egg and sharper at the other are said to be pyriform (pear-shaped); examples are those of lapwing, ringed plover, spotted sandpiper and murre. When in clutches eggs of this shape are economical of the space they occupy in the

Eight eggs of the common murre. Murre's eggs are always of the characteristic pyriform shape, but show great individual variation in markings and color. These are both adaptations to the murres' breeding habits. The shape makes the eggs less likely to roll accidently off the narrow, bare ledges on which they are laid. Their individually differing color patterns enable each pair of murres to recognize their own eggs. This ability is not possessed or needed by species that lay their eggs in nests or in less crowded situations.

nest; they fit snugly together with the sharp points to the center, like the whorl or leaves on a clover stem. The murre lays a single egg on a ledge unprotected by a nest, and, being pyriform, it does not roll far in one direction, but spins around in what a motorist would describe as a very tight lock. Other shapes are spherical, elliptical—a sphere pressed in around one equator—and sub-elliptical, which is halfway between elliptical and oval.

Reference to the murre's egg reminds me that it is sometimes mistaken for that of the great auk, its larger relative which has been extinct for over a hundred years. Very few great auk eggshells have been preserved and people who know that they are valuable keep a lookout for them in old forgotten collections. Records of sales show that they are valued at many hundreds of dollars. It may surprise you to hear that a great auk's egg is worth nearly 30 times its weight in gold. If anyone tells you they have one, it should measure about 5 in. in length; if the egg is about $3\frac{1}{4}$ in. it is a murre's.

INCUBATION

When a bird has laid the right number of eggs for the usual clutch for that species, no more are produced and the period of incubation begins. You may wonder (as others do) how a bird knows when it has produced enough eggs. It seems unlikely, for example, that it counts them over, because experiments have shown that birds are not good at counting. Nor is the number always, though possibly sometimes, predetermined in the ovary, because in a number of species tested experimentally the ovary has the capacity to produce many more eggs than are required for the normal clutch; domestic fowl and ducks of course are striking examples. Perhaps the bird just knows by the feel of the eggs under it that it has as many as it can cover easily. Possibly physiological changes, related to the action of settling down to incubate them, also put a brake on further egg production by the ovary.

Incubating eggs means attending to them in such a way as to provide the best conditions for the embryo to develop. One essential factor is keeping the temperature at a suitable level, and the optimum temperature for most eggs is, naturally enough, very near the body temperature of the parents. Birds sitting on eggs often have a bare area on the belly, a brood patch, so that eggs are in direct contact with the skin, and the skin in that area is sometimes heated with a special blood supply. The part played by each parent in the incubation of the eggs varies from one species to another. At one extreme there is, for example, the case of the mallard, where the drake, or cock, leaves the hen to sit on the eggs and bring up the chicks. He deserts her entirely, and although by our standards this seems rather cruel, by duck standards it is quite proper as there are good biological reasons. Such behavior is usual among most ducks and some game birds, the domestic fowl being a good example of the latter. In rare cases, in phalaropes, for example, like the northern phalarope, the female leaves the male to do all the incubating and family rearing. But in most species both sexes share the work in varying proportions. Sometimes, as in the mute swan, the male or cob, as he is called, remains on guard near the nest and if you trespass in his territory he is liable to attack, with quite painful consequences. Cocks not only afford protection but can also be helpful and attentive in bringing food to the sitting hens. It is interesting to note that in some species this important function is foreshadowed in pantomime in courtship displays—a behavior perhaps comparable with the human lover who brings gifts to the lady of his choice, as a token of his willingness to provide for her. The other alternative, of which there are many variations, is that cocks take their share of incubation, relieving the hens for longer or shorter periods. Sometimes the cocks seem fairly new to the job, for they only do short spells and may have no brood patch, but in others it is a long-established custom and the change-over is accompanied by pretty ritual displays. Cocks such as those of the finches and jays will occasionally be found brooding, but on the whole they leave this lonely vigil to the hen and sustain her with food. In many species the work is shared more or less equally, as in the grebes in which cock and hen do alternate spells of a few hours, and fulmar and common shearwater which do alternate long spells of up to several days.

What is going on inside the egg during incubation? It is comparable with what happens in the human uterus after conception, a new life is going through the first stages of development. Conception or fertilization in birds usually takes place when the ovum is released from the ovary and meets the sperm—millions of sperm although only one is needed—at the top end of the oviduct. At that stage of course there is nothing resembling the chick which will eventually emerge from the egg. After the union of the cells the minute germinal spot remains in a state of suspended development until it is stimulated into growth by incubation. Incidentally, occasional turning of the eggs and cooling off are as important as the heat supplied by the sitting bird. The cells of the germinal spot draw on the food stores and multiply rapidly. In due course all the main features of the adult take shape and the point is reached when the young bird must break out of the shell. The time taken by the embryo in development or the incubation period varies from one species to another. In the domestic fowl chicks appear in about 21 days. Most of the small birds, such as warblers, finches, sparrows, etc., take two weeks or less, ranging from 11 to 14 days. Nearly all the other common species range between two and four weeks. Only very few incubate for more than 30 days, by far the longest period or slowest in development being the petrels and shearwaters which take up to seven or eight weeks.

Young of Pacific loon.

CHAPTER II

Population

In the previous chapter I referred to some of the important matters connected with the breeding season. Males and females court, mate, build nests and rear families—perhaps two or three families when conditions are favorable. This takes place, in temperate climates, approximately in the spring and summer months which, in the north temperate region, is from March to August.

The timing of the various events of the breeding season differs from one species to another and even within the same species from one locality to another. The extent of this variation is not always known precisely. You could make a useful contribution to knowledge, as well as enjoy a fairly simple and fascinating exercise, which would provide an extra purpose in bird watching, by noting down at frequent intervals, at least once a day but oftener if possible, the activities of a pair of birds during the breeding season. It is fairly certain that you can find a pair within a short distance of your home; even if you live in a city a pair of robins may be nesting in a tree just outside your bedroom window. It does not matter if the bird you choose belongs to a common species, for in fact the common ones are often most neglected.

If you do keep a record, the time will come when you will make an entry that the young birds are fending for themselves and the parents are no longer interested in them. If it is a species that has only one brood in the season, or if it is the last brood of a species

which usually has more than one, then this marks the beginning of the nonbreeding season and at this time, and at this stage in these notes, it is a suitable occasion to consider various points relating to population.

ANNUAL FLUCTUATIONS

One point which may strike you is that there are far more birds at the end of the breeding season than there were at the beginning— the parents plus the young which survive from one or more broods—and yet at the beginning of the next breeding season you will find again only one pair, often the same birds, in approximately the same territory. Annual increase and decrease in the numbers of a species, of many mammals as well as birds, is a feature which is unusual to us.

In human society, in your town for example, births can occur any time throughout the year and the number of inhabitants is fairly constant, with, usually, a general tendency to increase gradually from one year to another. There is never any regular sudden increase. With birds it is quite a different matter: births, or hatchings, as we have seen, are concentrated in a short period. There is a quick growth in numbers and then a slow reduction until the lowest point is reached at the beginning of the next breeding season. The amount of annual fluctuation in bird population is perhaps much greater than you realize and the rapid increase is a factor which has an important bearing on other aspects of bird life. The main essentials of seasonal variation in numbers can be illustrated by what takes place in the mallard duck. I have tried to simplify and summarize the changes diagrammatically in Figs. 2-3.

The mallard generally begins to lay eggs about the first week in March: point X in the figure. An average clutch is 12 eggs, taking about 12 days to lay: the short

Figs. 2-3. Annual fluctuations in a population of mallard duck.
(Explanation in text.)

distance from X to the first dotted line. The potential population increase, therefore, is six times the number of the breeding population and the line XA is six times the length from X to the center of the figure. I should explain here that the solid black areas represent adult ducks and the wavy lines ducklings. The distances XY and AB indicate the incubation period, about four weeks. The line YB is shorter than XA because an average of only 10.8 chicks are obtained from

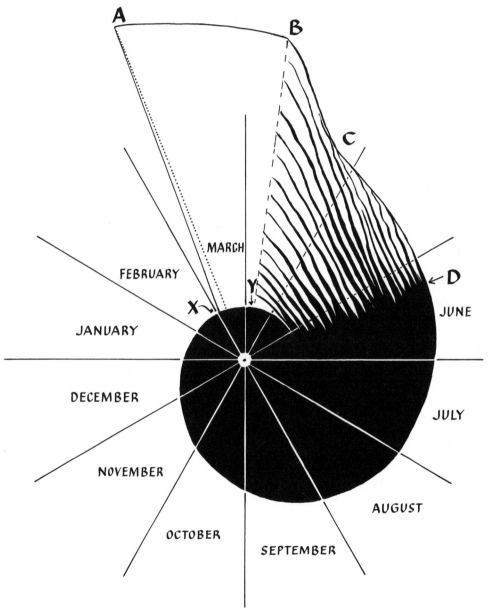

12 eggs (or 108 from 120 eggs to avoid splitting chicks!). Ducklings as you know are able to run about very soon after hatching so there is practically no nestling period; they become fledglings almost immediately and the wavy lines from B to D show the relative numbers and period of existence. In the first two weeks after hatching, B to C, the mortality is relatively very high for only 70 out of 108 chicks survive. Thereafter the mortality rate slows down and at the end of four months from hatching there are still five juveniles surviving from each clutch of 12 eggs. The chicks remain with the parents for about seven-and-a-half weeks, to point D on the figure. The area of black in each month shows the relative size of the population. I emphasize that the diagram is very much simplified, as a number of factors are not taken into account, but I think it gives a fairly reasonable picture of the enormous seasonal variation in the mallard; similar patterns could be obtained from a study of other species.

FOOD SUPPLY

Population fluctuations of this magnitude give rise to some problems which we do not think about in our own daily lives. For example, the hatching of the mallard chicks just mentioned would be like the sudden appearance of 500 young children in a village of 100 adults. A major problem would be how to feed them. Birds do not store food for this purpose. They rely entirely on what that can find from day to day. Perhaps I should qualify that statement for it is said that the nutcracker, for example, a European bird, does to some extent depend on the hazel nuts it stored in the autumn to feed its young in the following spring. But it seems that such habits are very rare and although tits, jays and nuthatches have also a marked tendency to hide food, in various places rather than in one large cache, the finding of it again is largely a matter of chance.

One way of trying to ensure a larder of adequate size to feed offspring is for a family to obtain the sole rights over an area of suit-able size where the right kind of food is available. It seems reasonable to believe, therefore, that the purposes of much territorial behavior is the staking of a claim on a piece of land where food resources can be exploited with the minimum of competition when the problems of family rearing begin. By that time the country suitable for occupation has been parcelled out and over-crowding is prevented. It is notable that when food is plentiful, individual territories tend to be smaller.

The demand for food is considerable as you will know if you have watched harassed parents relaying supplies to gaping mouths, and each chick can consume up to its own weight of food every day. Each bird must choose the right place and be able to time its breeding accurately to the food supply. How it does that is not fully understood.

POPULATION CONTROL

Population size in any species is the balance maintained between increase in numbers by reproduction and reduction in numbers due to various causes. Potentially 10 mallard (5 pairs) could increase their numbers in one year to 70 (10 plus 5 times 12 eggs hatched). Instead, as I have just shown (if we ignore annual fluctuations for the moment), the population at the beginning of the next breeding season is still only 10 birds. How many of the original 10 are replaced by young birds? If the average life of a mallard is 10 years (the information I have suggests that it is not less than that) then the wastage of adults is only 1 out of 10 each year. Therefore, only 1 out of about 30 juveniles, or 1 out of 60 eggs is required to maintain the mallard population.

That is a simple illustration in mathematical terms but actual examples of the high mortality and severe pruning which every species suffers are common enough when we look around. For instance, a pair of chaffinches bred in my father's garden on several successive years—in a rambler rose twisted round a trellis—and just as regularly every year a neighbor's cat raided the nest and got

Duck hunters are important predators on waterfowl everywhere. Ducks soon learn, however, to take full advantage of areas where they are protected from hunting as can be seen in this photograph of lesser scaups gathered in a South Texas arroyo. Sometimes, unfortunately, such crowding into safe refuges causes disease to spread.

at the chicks in spite of all reasonable efforts to protect them. Cats are important in controlling the numbers of many birds. Although we know it is natural for cats to take nestlings (adult birds too if they can catch them), we sometimes wish that it was from necessity.

This mortality can be, and is, and in fact must be high in order to keep most populations within reasonable bounds. In general terms, the amount of loss is equal to the amount of gain. In species with a high birth rate the mortality rate is equally high. This tremendous annual wastage of life is a fact which is sometimes difficult to appreciate. But is it really "wastage"? If we reflect for a moment we realize that, except in the case of cats and other domestic pets, the casualties

are the vital food of other animals. Some birds may live on the surplus population of certain caterpillars, but owls and other predators live on the surplus population of birds. These food chains, as they are called, make a very interesting study.

Control of the population of one species by another is quite natural. In normal circumstances a reasonable balance is maintained, but sometimes other factors do real harm by lowering the breeding population too far. It is these factors we have to watch. While it is the concern of various organizations dealing with protection and conservation, everyone must help too, if we are to preserve some species from extinction or at least disappearance from certain localities.

When the numbers of a bird in any locality remain much the same from year to year that species is said to be in a state of balance or equilibrium with its environment. I think it would be safe to say that the balance is never really steady. Something is always happening to upset it. It need not be, and indeed rarely is catastrophic, except perhaps in a very local sense when, for instance, a woodland is cut down or a marshy area drained or land is cleared for a new housing development. But from year to year there are many slight changes in environmental conditions which are to the advantage of one species and disadvantage of another, so that their populations decrease or increase. Sometimes it is possible to find fairly regular periodic fluctuations in numbers as, for example, in the ruffed grouse which seems to increase to a high peak roughly about every 10 years.

Slower changes over a long period of time are found in many species. The swallow-tailed kite was once common in many areas of the United States. Now it is found only in Florida and a few points along the Gulf Coast. You may find it difficult to believe that not so long ago the starling was quite an uncommon bird in places where it is now a nuisance because of its abundance. A few pair of starlings, which originally came from England, were released in Central Park in New York City in 1890. Since then they have spread as far as Alaska, California and Guatemala.

DISPERSAL

If the human population in your district becomes overcrowded, which means that there is not enough work for all and therefore not enough money to buy food, what happens? Usually some of the younger and more adventurous members of the community leave to seek their fortunes elsewhere. You will find that much the same sort of thing happens in the populations of many bird species. Observations have shown that the same pair of birds is likely to continue in occupation of a particular territory for several successive years, until one or both succumb to the natural hazards of existence. Of the chicks which survive to maturity, and are surplus to what the area can support, some may be expected to replace the casualties in the fixed population, and the rest may disperse to compete with others in the occupation of suitable habitats or to explore

the possibilities of new places to live in. The latter are the pioneers; that there is indeed such a category is illustrated by the fulmar colonization of British shores. Another interesting example is found in a recent account of attempts to colonize coastal waters by the velvet scoter in Finland, the velvet scoter being normally conditioned to breed in inland waters. In this unaccustomed environment the mortality was very high indeed; among chicks, for example, over 90 per cent died in the first few days after hatching. (Compare this with the usual mortality rate in the mallard—see Fig. 2.) Reading about this investigation brought to mind accounts of the hazards experienced by the early settlers in America as they pushed west to colonize new territory.

Each species has a fairly clearly defined distribution, habitat and habits and the steady competition by surplus population provides the incentive to extend and modify them. That seems to be a simple basic rule, but it is not equally simple and stable for all species at all times. In some the factors controlling the increase of population, often human interference, may be so strong that competition scarcely exists within the species. The golden eagle in America, for instance, appears to be just holding its own; the population is small, there is little increase in numbers from year to year and consequently little or no dispersal. A variant at the other extreme is one in which in some favorable season, or succession of seasons, there is a great increase in population and instead of a steady outward pressure there is a "flood"; great numbers burst the bounds of their normal range and pour into adjacent territory. This is one explanation of a phenomenon which is often called irruption or invasion, depending on which end you look at it from. (Another is the temporary move to unusual distances of large sections of a population because of occasional unsuitable living conditions.) In addition, humans may bring about changes in habitat as, for example, the importation of song birds, such as sparrow or starling, or of game birds such as pheasant.

CHAPTER III

Distribution

As WE ALL KNOW, many birds with which we are familiar where we live are not necessarily found in all other places. Those present and common in one locality may be present but rare in another or absent altogether. This means that the population of a species is not evenly distributed throughout its range, any more than people are evenly distributed in any county or country. Each species also has geographical limits. You will see, then, that there is both pattern of distribution (often call ecological distribution) and location of distribution (geographical distribution). Although they have some things in common I will refer to them separately. Ecological distribution, or birds in relation to their environments, will be the subject of the next chapter under the title "Habitats and Adaptations." Here I want to deal with some points relating to geographical distribution, or range.

SIZE OF RANGE

I will use the word "range" as a convenient substitute or synonym for the rather more cumbersome "geographical distribution." The range of a bird in this context includes all the localities in which it occurs regularly at some time or another throughout the year. Sometimes boundaries are clearly defined, as when a land bird reaches the sea. But often these boundaries are rather indefinite, birds

gradually becoming scarcer and fewer, their final limits varying from year to year depending on various factors, especially weather. The range includes the areas the bird occupies in the breeding and non-breeding seasons, and also it includes the country in between if there is a constant migrant passage.

Some ranges are very small. A good example is that of the sage grouse, a bird confined to the West and Midwest. Incidentally, it is a real American bird like the turkey, and is found in no other country. The golden eagle, chough, crested tit and others, which in England may be thought to be rare birds with their last strongholds in Britain, are found elsewhere, often in great numbers. The distribution of the red grouse is confined to Britain, mainly the heather moors of Scotland, Ireland, northern England and northern Wales.

There are many birds with much smaller populations. Two well-known examples from distant parts of the world are the takahe or notornis, a large kind of moorhen, which lives in remote valleys in the mountains of the south island of New Zealand, and the whooping crane of America. It is said that the populations of both are less than 100 birds. Although the range of the takahe is very small, a few square miles, that of the whooping crane is larger, because it migrates between breeding grounds somewhere in the vicinity of the Great Slave Lake in Canada and wintering grounds in the Aransas Wildlife Refuge of Texas.

There are other birds which in very large numbers occupy quite small breeding areas, and yet their ranges are very large. One of the most outstanding examples of this pattern is the great shearwater, a bird which can commonly be seen in offshore waters of our Atlantic coast, mainly in the spring months; this bird is known to breed only in the islands of the Tristan da Cunha group in the South Atlantic. It congregates there in immense numbers and after breeding disperses throughout the Atlantic as far north as Greenland. The gannet has a similar distribution pattern, but on a smaller scale, for its breeding grounds in Canada are limited to a few rocky islands, in the Gulf of St. Lawrence and off Newfoundland; it spreads out through many coastal waters as far as South America's coast; and it has similar breeding grounds off the shore of England. This kind of range is typical of seabirds, or rather oceanic birds, whose only contact with land is when they concentrate on some remote island or coast to breed and then disperse widely over the oceans.

By contrast most land birds spread out in their breeding areas, for reasons mentioned earlier, and those with large populations naturally occupy very extensive ranges. Two birds you may happen to be acquainted with have enormous ranges: the small barn owl and the oystercatcher. The latter in particular, a bird of open river banks, estuaries and coasts, where there is sand or gravel, is found in practically every country in the temperate and tropical regions of the world. This stoutly built bird with pied plumage, long red chisel-shaped bill, pink legs (usual colors) and, to me at least, peculiarly haunting cry, is as well known on rivers and coasts of New Zealand, Chile, Great Britain and New Guinea as it is in America. Its features are not exactly the same everywhere, any more than members of the human species are the same in every country, but the individuals are fundamentally the same (see Chapter X).

You might think that birds which we almost accept as essentially associated with our domestic life are universal in occurrence. But that is not so. The common English or "house" sparrow in fact does not occur everywhere in Britain, from where it came to America. There are occupied houses in many parts of the western isles of Scotland and in Ireland which have never had a house sparrow in their eaves: a famous naturalist once said that "a village without sparrows has as desolate an appearance as a house without children." The starling also is not widespread everywhere in America although it is rapidly extending its range. Many people who are not so very old will tell you that it is now common in places where it was rare or unknown in their young days. Both English sparrow and starling are essentially Old World species (Europe and Asia) but they have the distinction, shared also by a number of other species, of being assisted to extend their ranges. They are among the most notable birds introduced to the United States and New Zealand where they have settled down and thrived often at the expense of some native birds. They are regarded now as nuisances, although originally they gave much pleasure to early homesick settlers.

CONTINUITY OF DISTRIBUTION

An interesting side study in distribution is the extent to which members of a species keep in contact throughout their range. This can be looked at in two ways. What is the continuity of distribution in the breeding season, and what opportunities are there for intermingling in the nonbreeding season? These matters are important in the life of birds and study of them reveals a lot of information which can be used in the study of variation and evolution, referred to later in this book (see Chapter X). Here I wish merely to draw attention to the problem and to refer to a few points.

Regarding the continuity of distribution you might wonder, for example, if the English sparrows of New York, Boston, and

An adult and an immature whooping crane. Only a relatively few individuals of this large and spectacular species are now living. In spite of the serious and determined efforts being made to save it, it is in grave danger of extinction.

Montreal are linked by intermediate contacts so that, if such a thing were possible, a rumor started among those in one place would in time reach the others. This would be difficult to determine purely by field observations, but records of the recoveries of ringed or marked birds provide clues as to how much dispersal and intermingling usually takes place, even in birds which are considered to be quite sedentary. In widespread and common birds, and especially those which can live in different kinds of country or habitats there is probably much intermingling, but the English sparrow seems to be an exception.

In addition to what we can find out from banded birds there is much that can be deduced about continuity of distribution from a study of what individuals look like throughout the range of a species. When birds freely interbreed they remain much the same in appearance or there are gradual changes in character, like a piece of material in which the color is uniform or shaded from one color to another. A good example of the latter in Britain is found in the murre. Certain birds have a white ring around the eyes and a white streak behind it; this feature looks like a pair of white spectacles or a bridle, and birds which have it are called "bridled." This variety occurs in fairly regular proportions. In the Orkney Islands about 25 per cent of each breeding colony of murres are bridled, but the proportion decreases gradually southwards, and in colonies in southern Wales there is less than one per cent.

Breaks in the continuity of distribution are caused in various ways, as for example when a stretch of water forms a barrier to the dispersal of a sedentary land bird, like wrens. In most species however, even in very sedentary birds, there is evidence of a fair amount of interbreeding.

In the gannets of America there is no contact between some of the widely separated colonies during the breeding season, but there are opportunities for intermingling when the birds disperse in the nonbreeding season, and it is probable that matings take place between birds from the different colonies. It is uncertain what opportunities there are for the gannets of America to interbreed with their relatives on the other side of the Atlantic. It is possible that there may be a link through the colonies in Iceland, some of whose members may mate with birds from either side of the Atlantic. This may be rather a slender link, although as yet there is no evidence of isolation for all the gannets of the North Atlantic are similar in appearance. But if we look further afield we find gannets in South Africa which, both from the evidence of what is known about their range and the fact that they have distinctly different features, never mate with the North Atlantic birds. They are usually regarded as a different species. There is another closely related species of gannet in southeast Australia, with an outlying colony in the North Island of New Zealand.

The osprey presents a slightly different pattern. It is a land bird with a very wide range throughout the world and is fairly consistent in its features over extensive areas. The birds, which have been making efforts to settle in Scotland and whose ancestors at one time bred over most of Britain, are identical with those found throughout the whole extent of Europe and Asia as far as Kamchatka and Japan. The osprey is widely distributed through North America, but the birds have a slight though constant difference

in appearance and are regarded as "first cousins" or subspecies. There may be an interbreeding connection across the Bering Sea between Siberia and Alaska, but it is likely to be rather a slender one.

A good example of discontinuous distribution without change in character is found in a species of tree duck which occurs throughout many parts of Africa and is found also in South America. Specimens from both countries are quite indistinguishable. This case is especially interesting because it is unusual; on the whole the birds of South America are very different from those of Africa.

FAUNAL REGIONS

Reference to range and continuity of distribution leads to the more general subject of geographical or faunal regions. There were some species of birds I was familiar with in the north of Scotland but which occur, if at all, only rarely in the south of England. Their numbers are largely a matter of suitable environments. There are far more birds common to both places. Some areas in Britain might have one or two birds common there and rare or absent elsewhere, but the majority of birds are likely to be found in other places also. County lists of birds would contain many names common to most of them.

In Europe the situation is much the same. Many of the birds are the same as, or very like, common ones in England. A book on the identification of the birds of Britain would be quite useful almost anywhere in Europe. Only a few birds would be absent from the British list.

But how far outside Europe would a book like the popular *Field Guide to the Birds of Britain and Europe* be useful? It would be quite handy in China, would be fairly helpful in North America, not much use in Africa south of the Sahara, and pretty hopeless in South America and Australia. An American bird watcher would be more familiar with the birds of Japan than those of much nearer places, say, Dakar or Freetown in West

Africa, and especially of the Bahamas and Trinidad in the West Indies.

What this means is that there is only a little difference between the birds of Britain and those of other parts of Europe, but there is a much greater difference between those of Europe and of Africa. Most of the European birds recorded in Africa are ones which migrate regularly between the two countries, like cuckoo, swallow, nightjar, spotted flycatcher, garden warbler and others. Most birds resident in Africa, or at least the part of it south of the Sahara Desert which I will refer to presently as the Ethiopian Region (see Fig. 4), are peculiar to that country. But many African birds belong to groups or families also represented in Europe. A good example is found in the family of pigeons and doves, most of whose members you would recognize no matter where you met them. (Incidentally, the names "pigeon" and "dove" are merely alternative names for the same kinds of birds and not for distinct groups.) There are five representatives of this family in Europe, stock dove, rock dove, wood pigeon, turtle dove and collared dove,

the last now gradually extending its range westward into Britain. Only two of these penetrate into Africa south of the Sahara, but only just. In Africa there are about 40 other members of the family.

You will find that pattern repeated in other families: occasionally European representatives of a family have breeding populations in Africa, but the general rule is that the Sahara Desert forms a barrier to the distribution of species and when families are represented on both sides it is usually by distinct species. One other good example is found among game birds. In Europe there are birds like pheasant, partridge and red grouse, while in Africa it is a group of related species, the francolins, which are known as "pheasant" and "partridge" to people in Africa. In South America on the other hand game birds are mainly represented by the tinamous, birds of similar appearance and habits but not at all closely related. Of course many of these European and Asiatic game birds have been introduced for hunting purposes to many other parts of the world, particularly the United States.

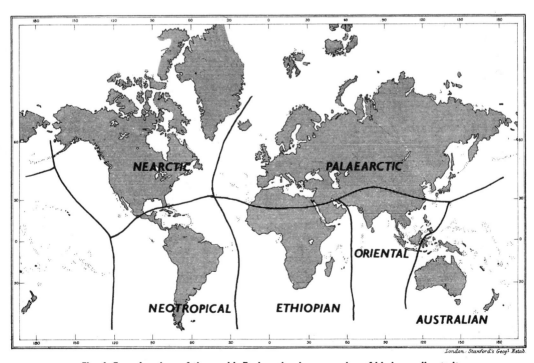

Fig. 4. Faunal regions of the world. Each region has a number of birds peculiar to it.

Africa has many birds belonging to families which are not represented in Europe at all. Parrots and hornbills are examples of familiar birds. But although these families do not have members in Europe they are not wholly confined to Africa. Hornbills are also found in India and southeast Asia, or the Oriental Region (see Fig. 4) and parrots (including parakeets, cockatoos, macaws, lovebirds and others) extend throughout the tropical regions of the world and some temperate regions like southern Australia and New Zealand.

What this adds up to is that the world can be divided into certain large areas or regions; a great percentage of birds belong in each region and nowhere else. Or put another way: there are about 8,500 known species of birds in the world (if there are any yet undiscovered they are few in number) and when the range of each is marked on a map it is found that many belong only to the New World or Old World or Australia or some other area. The actual faunal regions now recognized are shown in Fig. 4.

The regions are not all of equal status from the point of view of the birds peculiar (endemic) to them. The Oriental Region is not very clearly defined for it has no endemic family, although most of the 14 species of broadbills belong there. On the other hand, the Neotropical Region has 31 families which are found nowhere else. Some are quite large and important groups, like the tinamous (51 species), toucans (41 species), manakins (59 species), ovenbirds (209 species) and honeycreepers (36 species). Others consist of only one rare species, like the curious hoatzin with a clawed "finger" on the angle of its wing to assist the bird when it clambers about in the forests of British Guiana and adjacent places.

There are many similarities between the Nearctic and Palaearctic Regions, so much so that they are often combined into one region, the Holarctic. Their differences are of degree rather than of kind, and together they share a number of families which are not found elsewhere, birds like the loons, grouse, phalaropes, auks, waxwings and a family of 20 species, the *Regulidae*, several of whose members in North America have the name kinglet, and which in Britain is represented by two small birds with equally appropriate names, goldcrest and firecrest. The Nearctic has more affinities with the Palaearctic than with the Neotropical, although, as one would expect, the land bridge at Panama has been a highway for the distribution of a number of birds.

I cannot leave this fascinating subject without mentioning one of the most striking divisions between any two regions. You will see that the line I have drawn separating the Australian from the Oriental Region passes through the middle of the many islands which make up the East Indies. It passes in particular through the string of islands which form Indonesia. You might imagine that this is an average line and, like the one separating the Ethiopian or Oriental from the Palaearctic Region, it would not matter much if it were placed a little bit further to one side or the other. But far from it; this line, known as Wallace's Line after the famous naturalist explorer, A. R. Wallace, is a very definite one and a large proportion of the birds on each side of it are quite different from each other. In Indonesia it passes between the islands of Bali and Lombok which are little more than 10 miles apart. If you got to know all the birds on Bali you would be quite at sea with those on Lombok.

CHAPTER IV

Habitats and Adaptations

You will remember at the beginning of the previous chapter I mentioned "ecological distribution" or distribution in relation to particular kinds of environments, like woodland, seashore, rocky cliffs; or, on a larger scale, tropical forests, deserts, savanna, polar ice. I propose now to point out some of the more obvious ways in which birds are adapted for living in these places.

ANTARCTIC SEAS

There are few parts of the earth's surface which birds have not been able to colonize and there are few achievements which have attracted greater interest than the occupation of Antarctic seas by the penguins. The stories of early explorers and the reports of modern scientific expeditions are colored by tales and studies of these engaging creatures. By all accounts the wastes of ice and snow offer little attraction for human occupation, but penguins thrive there. How do they manage to do it?

The habitat offers no source of food on land, which is seldom exposed anyway. There is little in the way of vegetation or animal life to support bird life. The main source of food is the sea, which is relatively rich in animal life. The fish on which penguins mainly subsist have to be pursued by swimming and therefore, as there is little advantage or necessity in being able to fly, the penguins have become swimming birds. Other species like cormorants, grebes and divers pursue fish under water and can also fly, but by keeping a foot in both camps—or a wing in both elements—they are not as expert as they might be in either. The penguins are highly efficient swimming birds.

One of the most important adaptations of penguins to life in Antarctic seas is, therefore,

Fig. 5. Antarctic Penguin and Arctic Great Auk (now extinct): two birds from opposite poles which look very alike because they are adapted for living in similar conditions.

Gentoo penguins leaping out of the sea onto the ice. Other species of penguins also practice this method if the level of the ice or shore on which they wish to land is too high above the sea for them to walk out. Often, if the sea is rough, a penguin may have to make several attempts before it succeeds. In doing this, the penguin is often swept about by the waves and buffeted against ice or rocks, but its dense, thick plumage acts as a shock absorber and usually saves it from injury in such circumstances.

(Above) The small and dainty fairy penguins are found around the coasts of New Zealand and southern Australia. The close, dense feathering and short, paddle-like wings, adapted for "flying" under water—not in the air—are similar to those of all other penguins.

the modification of wings for swimming instead of flying. It is generally believed that penguins are descended from birds which once could fly; although this transition must have taken place a very long time ago there are many pointers indicating that penguins evolved in this way, not least of which is the evidence of similar tendencies at the present time. The evidence is found in members of the auk family which are the equivalents of penguins in the Arctic, but in a less advanced stage of evolution. The most penguin-like member is, or was (for it has recently become extinct), the great auk. Incidentally the name penguin belonged to the great auk, and still does in French.

The great auk was flightless and its general build and appearance closely resembled the penguin. In both, the pinions or flight feathers are much reduced in size (in penguins they are little more than a short stubble) and the whole wing or forearm is modified into a paddle. They are similar to the paddle-like forelimbs of seals and other sea mammals and not unlike the anterior fins of fish. It is an interesting reflection that in the course of evolution some birds should revert to resemble their fish ancestors which lived in the days when there were no land animals at all.

Because the great auk could not fly it

These comical-looking auklets, together with the murres, dovekies and puffins, take the place of the penguins in northern seas. They can all fly and most breed either on steep cliffs or rocky slopes difficult of access for man or other mammals. The extinct great auk was a member of this family that had, like the penguins, become completely adapted to the water and was unable to fly. As a result it bred on low-lying islands and skerries where it was easily killed and finally exterminated by man.

29

became an easy prey to human predators, who found it a valuable source of food and oil. Fortunately for penguins they lived far enough away to be immune from exploitation in an age when little thought was given to preservation. No doubt they also would have suffered, for the flesh is said to be palatable and they are well supplied with fat, like blubber on seals and whales. The fat layer serves the same purpose in each in protecting the body from the intense cold; in penguins it supplements the feathers whose primary function, as in all birds, is to provide warmth.

The adaptations of many penguins to resist cold are well illustrated at breeding time. In birds with which we are acquainted we usually associate the period of nesting and incubation with the warm days of spring and early summer; but some penguins, especially the emperor penguin, the largest and toughest of them all, breed in the depth of the Antarctic winter. They stoically incubate their single egg through blizzards and low temperatures which no other living creature could survive, at the same time providing sufficient warmth from their bodies for the embryo to develop and the chick to hatch. The emperor and king penguins do not sit on their single egg, but balance it on their feet and envelop it with a special fold of skin on the belly so that it is completely protected. Surely this is one of the most striking examples of adaptation of any animal to an environment which appears to be completely uninhabitable. Unlike its human counterpart, the Eskimo, who builds an igloo, the penguins do not burrow in ice or snow, but sit out fully exposed to the worst the elements can do.

THE OCEANS

The wide expanses of the oceans are another very uniform type of habitat covering a great part of the earth's surface, seven-tenths of it in fact. They present a problem in colonization which a number of birds have attempted to solve. The birds which come to mind in particular are the albatrosses. They are the most notable ocean wanderers, though not necessarily the most successful. Many of the less spectacular shearwaters and petrels, including the little storm petrel or Mother Carey's chicken, are so well adapted to this environment that they spend the greater part of their lives on the open seas out of sight of land; they visit land only to breed. Even for breeding purposes, some birds are so out of touch with life on land that they sneak in and out of their nests at night, as

Black-footed albatrosses in flight. When not at their island nesting places albatrosses, like their relatives the shearwaters and petrels, spend their time at sea. At least during the daylight hours, they are usually in flight, gliding over the waves.

does the Manx shearwater. This habit is in fact a protective one because the birds flounder about so helplessly on land that they are an easy prey to the predators which could make havoc among them in the daylight hours.

You are unlikely to see albatrosses anywhere in the North Atlantic although, as usual, there are exceptions to every general statement. Except for two species which live in the North Pacific the home of the members of this family is the southern oceans. The species best known because of its size and the story of the "Ancient Mariner" is the wandering albatross. It ranges from the pack ice of the Antarctic up to 20 degrees south latitude. Its northern limit is quite well defined, a fact I had the pleasure of proving to my own satisfaction when sailing on one occasion to Cape Town. I watched the daily progress of the ship on the chart posted for the interest of passengers, until one day I could say that on the next we should be seeing albatrosses. Sure enough they came around the ship the next day and thereafter were in constant attendance. It is an intriguing problem to understand how a bird knows the limit of its range on a featureless ocean. It is possible that the limit may be defined by the availability of food and the amount of energy necessary to be expended to get it. It is uneconomical for a bird, or any animal, to use more energy in looking for food than it can replace by the food it gets. Energy can, of course, be stored in the form of fat which can be expended without replacement, as happens with many birds which go on long migration flights.

The success of the albatrosses in colonizing the oceans rests mainly in their ability to travel great distances with the expenditure of very little energy. It is important also that they have adapted their physiology so that they do not require fresh water to drink, as many inshore seabirds do. They have found a way of eliminating salt from the sea water they take in, either by intentional drinking or in the course of feeding, by means of a gland in the nose which acts as an auxiliary kidney. But the most striking adaptation is the flight of the great albatrosses. These birds are like sailing ships which rely mainly on air currents for movement and do not consume large quantities of fuel to keep them going. They are more like gliders, or more correctly they are superb gliders, for they sweep over the oceans for hours on end in effortless movement. There are many accounts by observers on ships who have carefully watched an albatross for long periods, and who maintain that the bird not once made any visible effort to keep in the air by flapping its wings. Flapping is necessary for rising off the water and, as in the case of the large swans, the maneuver can be difficult and laborious, unless assisted by a fair amount of wind to take off into. Albatrosses are experts in the use of air movements, gaining elevation from the upward currents which rise from the side of waves facing the wind. From the height gained they glide forward in whatever direction suits them, down to the surface of the sea, and then up again as before.

Albatrosses' wings are long and narrow, unlike some land "gliders" (such as eagles and vultures whose wings are typically broad), and the wandering albatross has the distinction of possessing the greatest wing span of all birds. It is about 11 to 12 ft., twice the height of a tall man or about the width of a medium-sized room. Its weight of about 16 lbs. is surpassed by that of the mute swan which is about 20 to 25 lbs. I think it is only fair to the parties concerned to say that although sailors are traditionally more superstitious than most people there seems to be no foundation for the one which Coleridge puts into the mouth of the Ancient Mariner; apparently sailors have never considered it unlucky to kill an albatross. Coleridge invented the story, but of course that does not detract from the interest of the poem.

There are, as I have said, quite a number of successful ocean colonizers, if I might use that word for birds which must of necessity breed on land although they spend the greater part of their lives at sea. There are frigate birds or man-o'-war birds, tropic birds, gannets and boobies, auks, skuas, some gulls and terns, and others. They have been classified into three main groups, the inshore birds which seldom go out of sight of land, offshore birds which go further out to sea, about as far as the continental shelf in the Western European area, and oceanic or pelagic birds.

OTHER AQUATIC HAUNTS

Penguins, albatrosses and other oceanic species are birds which have become adapted to aquatic habitats of uniform and rather vast dimensions. There are a number of other haunts associated with water, both salt and fresh, much favored by birds many of which have special features enabling them to live there.

Returning for a moment to the penguins, one of their interesting features, which contributes largely towards their amusing resemblance to people, is their upright carriage. They usually stand and walk with the long axis of the body in a vertical position, whereas in most other birds it is nearly horizontal. You may have wondered about this. It is a question of balance and is due to the fact that the legs of penguins are placed far back towards the tail-end of the body. This is an adaptation to aquatic life; it is like having the paddle or propeller of a boat at the stern, and is found in various stages of development in many other water birds. You can see an early stage of it in some of the ducks, especially when a duck, slowly waddling along, is made to go faster. It is well developed in cormorants, murres, grebes and especially in loons. Loons have their legs so far back that they are awkward on land; they can scarcely walk upright, but do sometimes, and at other times heave themselves along on their bellies, as penguins do in the snow as a change from walking.

Most water birds, of course, have webbed feet. The skin between the toes is extended to varying lengths in different species so that in water the foot becomes a paddle, and a very

efficient one it can be. If you can observe the action, as is sometimes possible in the case of a swan when it swims near you in fairly clear water, you will see that in the forward movement the toes are closed and curved and present the minimum of resistance, but in the backward stroke the toes splay out and a strong backward kick propels the bird forward at a good speed.

Not all water birds have this web-footed adaptation. Another type of paddle has been evolved, especially by the grebes, and, judging by their numbers and the world-wide distribution of the 18 species, the adaptation seems to be quite a successful one. Instead of webs each toe has extensions of the skin to form lobes, like a series of small paddles; these enable the bird to push its way through the water. The coot also, and related species, which belong to quite a different family, have developed this curious type of lobed-toed feet.

Perhaps I can take this opportunity to mention that the term used to describe the occurrence of similar structures in widely different species is "convergent evolution." Many similarities in species are due to the fact that they inherited them from a common recent ancestor. Swallows and martins, for example, are in this category, but both are far removed from the swifts which they resemble very closely; indeed some species of swifts and swallows are so alike that it can be quite difficult to say to which group they belong.

Webbed and lobed feet are adaptations in birds which spend much of their time swimming. Birds which have these features mainly frequent the open deep waters. Another distinct type of watery habitat is one in which shallow water is associated with a rich growth of vegetation, as in marshes and swamps, and here we find, among a number of adaptations, another kind of foot modification. In these habitats, where there is often very little open water, birds have less need to swim than to balance and walk on floating vegetation. Long toes enable them to do this for they distribute the weight in the same way that snowshoes distribute the

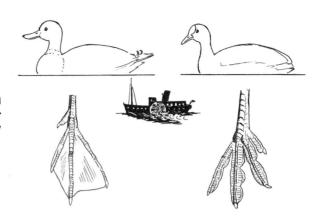

Fig. 6. Webbed foot of mallard duck and lobed foot of coot: different adaptations for the same purpose—progressions on water by paddling.

weight of a man so that he can walk on soft snow. The snow-shoe type of foot is found in the gallinule or moorhen, and various rails; you will see an excellent illustration of it in use if you get an opportunity to observe gallinules feeding in a pond of waterlilies. This adaptation reaches its greatest development in a group of birds called jacanas or lily-trotters which inhabit tropical swamps. In one species, the African jacana of the Nile Sudd and other swamps, each foot covers an area of about 8 in. diameter and yet the bird's body is only about 10 in. long, or about the size of a snipe.

Many birds find a rich supply of food in the shallow margins of inland and coastal waters and, in the way fishermen do, they find it an advantage to wade into the water. This practice has led to the evolution of the long-legged wading birds. Although the name "wader" is often used for a particular group of birds in which many species have this habit, birds like curlew, godwit, sandpiper and others, it is not peculiar to them. There are waders in many other groups and a typical example is the great blue heron, a bird which paces cautiously in the shallows on the alert to spear with its long pointed bill any unwary fish which comes within its range. A well-known example of highly specialized wader is the familiar flamingo with its long stilt-like legs, long neck, white plumage with pink tint and curious bill adapted for use upside down.

The flamingo type of bill, which is used

for sifting edible morsels from muddy water, is usual in most ducks, especially the shoveler whose bill capacity is increased by being wider at the tip, an adaptation which is even more highly developed in the spoonbill (Fig. 10). The bills of most of the wader group, including many species which do not actually stand in water but forage on the seashore and other places, are long and thin and adapted for probing in soft, wet places. It is fascinating to watch an oystercatcher on the sands at ebb tide as it selects one spot after another and at each plunges its bill in at different angles. A variation of the probe is the chisel type of bill, like that of the turnstone, which is adapted for rougher kinds of work, tipping over stones and pebbles on the beach in search of various insects, crustacea and other edible morsels.

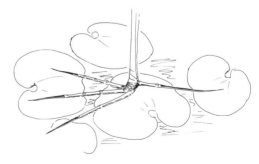

Fig. 7. Long toes of the lily-trotter or Jacana, an adaptation for distributing weight when walking on floating vegetation.

CLIFF HABITATS

A number of birds frequent two different kinds of habitats and show adaptations for both. This is particularly true of sea birds all of which must nest on land. Favorite nesting places are cliffs and rocky islets where ledges and cracks provide what often seems to be rather meager accommodation. Members of the auk family in particular are associated with these places. Murre and razorbill deposit their single eggs on precarious ledges, a habit which is in itself a protective adaptation against would-be predators. Although you might conclude that there should be a high percentage of fatal accidents, the pyriform shape of the eggs makes them less liable to roll off the edge. Nestlings are relatively inactive creatures until they have grown enough to move without becoming casualties.

Northern or Brünnich's murres on their nesting cliff. This species is like the common murre in appearance and habits, but has a thicker bill and breeds further north.

The puffin, or sea parrot, so called because of its curious large bill which gives it a kind of pompous expression, is another member of the auk family which makes its home on cliffs. Its special niche is at the top of the cliff where there is soil for burrows or where there are ready-made holes. Gannets also and the kittiwake and other gulls are dwellers in crowded rocky tenements. They are popular habitats mainly because of the relative freedom enjoyed by the occupiers from interference by predators. But they are not quite immune from attack, for raven, crow, skua, peregrine falcon and buzzard take their toll in one way and another. There is a constant struggle, defense and attack, as there is in human society.

FORESTS AND WOODLANDS

Forests and woodlands and the adaptations of the birds associated with them are a very large subject. For one thing birds, like ourselves, are believed to have originated from ancestors which lived in trees. Tree habitats, therefore, are many and varied, from the jungles of the Amazon and Congo to the pines and spruces of the cold north.

There are two general characteristics common to most forest birds, especially those which live in the trees as distinct from those which keep to the forest floor. Forest birds are often gaily colored. Perhaps the most striking example of this is found in the birds of paradise of the New Guinea forests. Some males have the most brilliant colors and color patterns to be found anywhere in nature. Then there are trogons, toucans, touracos, barbets and woodpeckers, the last including the northern representatives of this very large family; also the nuthatch, tanager and other woodland species are among our most colorful birds.

The other general feature of woodland birds is the modification of feet so that they can take a good grip on twigs, branches and bark. Often feet are large and strong, because many forest birds are as nimble as monkeys and run and clamber about among the branches. Parrots show this very well; you may have seen how they climb about their cages. I wonder if you have noticed that instead of having three toes in front and one behind, the usual arrangement, they have two in front and two behind (called zygo-dactylous), a useful adaptation for getting a good grip around a bough.

Even the magnificent birds of paradise in their brilliant plumes have large coarse legs and feet; they are like fabulously beautiful aristocrats with the hands of manual laborers. The natives of New Guinea, when they collected these birds for decorative purposes, cut off the ugly feet. This gave rise to the belief held by early travelers that these beautiful birds lived perpetually in the air—hence the name, bird of paradise, and scienti-

fic name, *Paradisea apoda*, or paradise bird without feet.

In Britain there is now very little virgin forest. The last vestiges of the Caledonian pine forests in the region of the Cairngorm Mountains are becoming as rare as one of their most interesting inhabitants, the crested tit. All the British tits, except the bearded tit of the fens, are woodland birds and are adapted for foraging for insects among twigs and branches. But perhaps the nuthatches, creepers and woodpeckers are the most typical woodland birds. The nuthatches are noted for their exceptional ability of walking down tree trunks as well as up them. This is a feat which has been mastered by few birds, or animals; perhaps you will have noticed how a cat sometimes gets "treed," for although it can hook its claws in to get up the tree it is in a quandary how to get down until it learns the art of coming down backwards.

The brown creeper, like the cat, can only climb up; it is a characteristic of this bird that it flies to the base of a tree, works its way up, then flies to the base of another. Its special adaptation is a tail whose feathers have the central shaft or rhachis stiffened so that the tail functions as a bracket propping the bird against the tree. Woodpeckers also have this adaptation, but it is interesting to note that the green woodpecker in Britain, perhaps because of the continual reduction in timbered area, is getting accustomed to forage on the ground for the ants, for which it has a special liking. Perhaps in time it will become completely divorced from trees, as has a relative in South Africa which lives on the ground in treeless country.

SOME GROUND BIRDS

Like the ground woodpecker, there are many birds which spend most of their lives on the ground, or at least never alight in bushes and trees. Ground species are believed to have evolved from forest birds. It is possible that even the ancestor of the ostrich, which was almost certainly a flying bird (although then it must have been a very much smaller type), was a bird which lived in trees. However, that is a matter on which there is no certain information.

Ground birds have a number of adaptations to the many varied habitats they frequent, but one which is common to most of them is camouflage. Their colors match those of their environments, and when they remain perfectly still they are very difficult to see. This is especially true of birds living in exposed places. The way of it seems to be this. It is the lot of most birds, and animals, to be preyed on by others, and there are several general kinds of ways of outwitting the attacker. One is by moving faster, in the way that ostrich and gazelle try to escape the lion and leopard, and the pigeon the peregrine falcon. Another way of escape is by taking cover and playing hide-and-seek among undergrowth and the thick foliage of bushes and trees. Neither of these is very suitable to many birds living in open country. Small birds unable to fly fast, and even fast-flying birds when they brood on exposed nests, must rely on camouflage. While studying birds in desert areas I have had practical experience of how invisible some can be. Birds have landed within yards of me and seemed to disappear right into the background. An effort of concentration was necessary to locate them. If I had not known they must be there I would easily have walked past them while carefully watching.

Many brooding birds are quite exposed, but it requires a lot of patience to locate them. Sometimes, when you do find them, the birds are so conditioned to remaining immobile that you can stroke them and even lift them off the nest.

One of the best examples of camouflage in open country in the north is the ptarmigan, which lives on bare tundra. The ptarmigan camouflages itself, even molting into pure white plumage in winter to match the color of the snow.

The ptarmigan and many other game birds provide an interesting example of ground species with varied habitats and adaptations. The bare bleak tops of many of the Scottish mountains, mainly above 2,000 feet, and the northern tundra in Canada are the haunts of the rock ptarmigan. Below this level it is replaced in Scotland by the red grouse on the heather slopes and high moors, and in Canada by the spruce grouse of the northern forests. The black grouse in Britain favors the lower edges of the moors and rough outlying pastures where there are scattered bushes and trees. The ruffed grouse of the American continent prefers open woodland, while the prairie chicken used to be abundant in open areas of the East but is now found mainly in the Western plains. Our turkey, Scotland's capercaillie, and the originally Asiatic pheasant are birds of the forest and woodland where they keep mainly to the ground though the capercaillie, in particular, flies into trees. The wild turkey likes woodland in which 10 to 25 per cent of the trees have been cleared, the haunts of the capercaillie are the coniferous forests, while those of the pheasant are typically copses, spinneys and plantations. Many game birds in the United States, such as bobwhite and Hungarian partridge, are associated with cultivated areas.

CHAPTER V

Adaptations for Flight

THE BRIEF SURVEY of habitats and adaptations outlined in the previous chapter will give you an inkling of the wealth of interest there is in this subject. There are at least 8,500 different kinds of birds in the world; each fits into a particular niche in its environment and does so by virtue of its special adaptations. Differences between species are sometimes very great; think, for example, of the great variety of beaks they have, the thin delicate beaks of the warblers, thick beaks of finches, probe-like beaks of some waders, chisel-like beaks of woodpeckers, enormous beaks of hornbills, grotesque beaks of pelicans. Multiply this by other features. But among all the differences of habitats and their related adaptations there is one environment they share in common: the air. Special modifications of structure have been evolved in birds in order to make use of it. Even those birds which do not fly now, like kiwi, ostrich and penguins, are descended from ancestors which did fly. Adaptations for flight have made birds a unique group in the animal world. What are these modifications?

FEATHERS

Flight and feathers seem almost synonymous. It is easy to imagine that birds have feathers because they fly, but it is in fact the other way around. Birds had feathers before they flew. The original use of feathers, which were much simpler in structure than many of them are now, was to provide a warm covering for the body, as hair does in most mammals. When the primitive reptilian ancestors of birds became active and warm-blooded, they required some covering to protect them from loss of heat in conditions where the temperature varied.

You probably know that snakes and frogs and other reptiles and amphibians are cold-blooded, which means that the temperature of their blood is always the same as the temperature of their surroundings. If their environment is cold they also are cold. But they do not feel cold, any more than you feel your bath water cold, or hot, when it is at the same temperature as your body. Therefore frogs and snakes and the reptilian ancestors of birds did not require a covering to keep them warm.

Flying birds evolved with a body covering of feathers, primarily to keep them warm. (Feathers are described in the next chapter.) Some feathers, like the main wing and tail feathers, have lost their original function, to become essential for flight. It should be remembered that such changes took place over a very long period of time, and no doubt improvements are still proceeding at the imperceptibly slow rate of evolution. The first use of feathers in aiding birds to become airborne was for gliding. The generations of reptiles which gradually became birds learned to glide long before they could flap their wings vigorously enough to rise from the ground and propel themselves through the air. Self-propulsion required lots of other modifications, some of which I will mention presently.

The difference between gliding and flying is illustrated by the man-made glider and airplane, the one making use of outside forces, gravity and air currents, and the other generating its own. The oldest known bird, *Archaeopteryx*, was a glider. Although it was clearly a bird, and a highly evolved one at that, the evidence of its structure suggests that it was not an active flyer. If it was in the direct line of descent many thousands of years must have followed before its offspring became self-propelled.

Feathers, of course, are not essential for flight. Bats are flying mammals with hair not feathers, but the hairy protective covering of the mammals they descended from did not become modified in the way feathers did. Perhaps that is why there are fewer flying mammals than birds. There is no doubt that feathers proved to be an important aid in the evolution of flight.

WEIGHT REDUCTION

Feathers also have the property of lightness, and weight is of critical importance in flight. When you travel by air you are told that you are allowed only a certain small weight of luggage, whereas when you go by train no limits are fixed, within reason. Birds learned this rule a very long time ago, not consciously, and took all kinds of measures to lighten their weight.

Small size

One way to reduce weight is to become smaller. Birds are relatively small animals, at least, the flying ones are. Among the many species of birds you will notice that by far the

The cassowaries of New Guinea and northern Australia are the only very large flightless birds that inhabit tropical jungles. The hard, bony helmet probably serves to protect the bird's head when it is forcing its way through dense undergrowth. The bare skin on the neck is brilliantly colored. Some New Guinea natives often rear cassowary chicks, but such hand-reared cassowaries are, when adult, extremely dangerous to human beings because they do not fear to attack with their formidable feet and bill.

A herring gull in flight. It is beginning to check its forward movement, in preparation either to land or to swoop down and pick up food. This can be seen from the partly lowered position of the legs.

The same herring gull a second or so later. It has now brought its legs further forward and fully spread and partly depressed its tail, thus still further decreasing its speed.

greater number, in population as well as in kinds, are of small size. Think of the numerous small warblers, finches, buntings, flycatchers, and various members of the thrush family. In tropical countries there are swarms of tiny hummingbirds and sunbirds, many of them not much bigger than large insects. There are relatively few large birds, like the golden eagle and various swans and geese. Swans take wing infrequently, and then often with reluctance, and apparently with considerable effort, although when airborne they fly well; they are not like the English sparrow, for instance, which scarcely moves a yard without flying.

The really large birds are flightless, like ostrich, emu and cassowary, and the recently extinct moa, which was at least twice the height of a man. There are reasons for believing that flightless birds are descended from flying birds which for some reason or another—probably the absence of ground enemies—gave up flying. It seems equally certain that these ancestors could not have been as large as the modern flightless forms descended from them. It would be difficult, if not impossible, for a bird the size and

weight of an ostrich to fly. The wing area would have to be enormous and the muscles necessary to operate them equally great. There is in fact an economical limit to the size a flying bird can be. If there was any tendency in the progress of evolution for the ostrich to become a flying bird again, it is pretty certain that it would begin by becoming smaller.

Light construction

Much of the success in airplane construction is due to the discovery of lightweight but strong metal alloys; so also with birds the conquest of the air has been greatly assisted by reduction in the weight of various parts of their anatomy. I wonder if you have noticed how light bird bones are. Lightness is one of their most typical characteristics. If, in the country, you come across a bone, especially one of the main arm or leg bones, like humerus or femur, which might seem to belong to either bird or mammal, it is usually possible to make a good guess which it is by means of this lightness test.

Another clue to identity of bird bones is to be found in the fact that most are hollow and thin walled, whereas mammal bones usually contain marrow, or show evidence of having contained it, and look very solid. The hollows in pneumatic bird bones are occupied by balloon-like extensions from the lungs, called air sacs (see page 59); these thin-walled membranes would obviously be dried out and not be visible in old bones. Although air sacs and their extensions into bones have other important functions, they do also contribute to the lightness of birds by decreasing the weight to volume ratio, and in a negative way by occupying parts of the bird's body which might otherwise be filled with heavier materials.

Egg-laying

In what other ways do birds keep their weight down? An interesting method is found in their reproductive habits. Egg-laying is primitive and often very wasteful. It would have been in keeping with other improvements in bird evolution if they abandoned this practice in favor of a more economical one, as mammals did. But they retained it, seemingly for the very good reason that it would have been difficult or impossible to fly, or at least it would have greatly hampered birds' movements in the air if they had to fly around weighted down with several embryo nestlings, like a cat with kittens. Weight would be increased not only by the embryos, but also by the additional amount of food required to be eaten in order to nourish them in the gestation period.

While egg-laying is a wasteful habit that birds have retained, they have modified it in order to make it more economical. They have reduced the number of eggs necessary to be laid in order for each species to survive; they are not as prodigal with eggs as fish are for example. Then they have developed the habit of looking after their eggs and of giving careful attention to the chicks which hatch from them, as I mentioned in Chapter I on parental care.

Birds have even altered the method of laying eggs which is usual in most egg-laying animals. They do not collect in their abdomen all the required number and then deposit them all at once, or at least in large batches, as most reptiles do. They produce only one egg at a time, and then deposit it as quickly as possible. In the domestic hen, for example, it is known that the normal time between ovulation, when the ovum is released from the ovary, and deposition or laying is about 26 hours—and what an amazingly complex structure is built up in that time! (See page 10.)

Birds, therefore, are very light in relation to their volume. They are much lighter than many people realize, or even believe, judging by the number of times I am asked to settle arguments. Guessing the weight of a bird seems to be one of the perpetual riddles, like the width of a penny and many other similar queries, with which those who know the answers like to mystify their friends. In my experience the answer disputed by the incredulous is usually the weight of a sea gull, although the questioner is often unaware of the fact that there are several species of gulls of very varied size. Many birds certainly look as if they ought to be much heavier than they really are, but this is partly accounted for by their thick layer of light feathers, which is sometimes fluffed out. A herring gull will weigh about $2\frac{1}{2}$ lbs., incidentally.

RIGID SKELETON

Small size, lightweight construction and the modification of feathers, into pinions in particular, are all adaptations for flight, but there are a number of others equally important though perhaps less obvious. They are mainly connected with the features of the internal anatomy of birds, and as these parts will be described more fully in later chapters, I will make only brief reference here to a few important points.

One point is that although bird bones are lighter than mammal bones of similar size they are not any less strong; they conform to the general principle that a metal tube can be as strong as a solid piece of the same diameter. Also bird bones are closely knit together into a skeleton which is very rigid and yet quite flexible at its joints. Rigidity, for instance, is found particularly in the pelvic girdle which forms a solid unit with a section of fused vertebrae, the synsacrum. Without this rigidity, considerable strain would be put on the muscles and tendons required to support the parts of a more or less horizontal body suspended between two uprights, the legs. Also sudden shocks conveyed by the legs to the pelvis would strain it when a bird makes a heavy landing, as it must do sometimes, and most surely did long ago when its ancestors were first learning to fly.

The pectoral girdle also is a curiously rigid and basket-like structure. Anyone who has eaten a chicken will have noticed an important feature, one which is particularly associated with birds, though vaguely suggested also in bats, namely the deeply keeled breastbone or sternum. This is associated with the development of the large breast muscles which are required to work the wings. These muscles must have an equally large and solid foundation, and in order to provide this base the breastbone has grown this deep keel. Flightless birds do not have a keeled sternum. Although the bones which form the pectoral girdle are built into a solid basket the sternum moves up and down in relation to the backbone, like the arms of an old-fashioned bellows. This is for much the same purpose, because this action helps to supply oxygen to the lungs, as the bellows do to the fire.

OXYGEN SUPPLY

Perhaps one of the most outstanding adaptations connected with bird flight is the manner in which birds breathe. It is still a source of great interest to biologists and, so far as I know, the exact details of what takes place are not fully understood. However, the general principle is fairly clear. In the first place the lungs do not expand and contract as ours do in breathing. Air circulates through them. This is not an easy fact to grasp because air goes in and out of the bird's nostrils just as in ours and the breast or sternum often "heaves" in unison with this action.

A curious feature of bird lungs is that the tubes are not branched like a tree, as in mammal lungs, but are connected in circuits, like the coils of tubes in a radiator. When a bird breathes in, fresh air—air charged with oxygen—circulates through these tubes. The oxygen is extracted for use in the tissues, and at the same time a large amount is by-passed into numerous large air reservoirs or air sacs (see page 59). Pressure on these containers, as when the breast is compressed during breathing out, forces this fresh air along the tubes, so that oxygen is again available for extraction. This means that there is fresh air in the lungs both when a bird breathes in and when it breathes out.

You may well wonder why birds require so much oxygen. The reason is that a tremendous amount of energy is needed to activate wing muscles and the usual method of breathing would not supply oxygen quickly enough. It will be abundantly clear to you that much more energy is required to lift a garden roller off the lawn than to propel it along a level surface; likewise a bird uses more fuel in rising into the air than an animal of the same size would use in starting to walk. Think also of the essential engine size and fuel consumption of a car compared with that of an airplane capable of carrying the same weight.

EFFICIENT HEART

It would not be much use having lungs to extract large quantities of oxygen from the air unless there were also an equally efficient means to convey this material to the muscles where it is required. The conveying medium is, as you know, the blood, and this is kept in rapid circulation by a relatively large heart which can increase its rate of pumping far beyond anything ours can do even when we run our hardest. The bird's heart also, like ours, is efficient in pumping to the muscles blood which has been freed from impurities. Incidentally, unlike an internal combustion engine in which fuel and exhaust systems are separate, the blood in all vertebrates is the conveyor of both the oxygen fuel and the carbon dioxide exhaust products which result when it is converted into energy; how the two functions are separated in higher animals, including birds, is explained briefly on page 60.

ADEQUATE COOLING

I have just said that when birds flap their wings vigorously, as they usually have to when they rise into the air, much fuel and oxygen is consumed. A product of this activity is heat. Far more heat is generated than is required for ordinary purposes and, therefore, the bird must have some means of dispersing the surplus; it must have an efficient cooling system. This is easily understood when you think what happens when you run hard; you get hot, you perspire, and the evaporation of this moisture cools you; if you are running in a race you wear as few clothes as possible so that sweat can evaporate more freely. If you tried to run in ordinary weather, wrapped in a feather quilt, you would give up very soon from heat exhaustion. But birds have to fly wrapped in feathers.

It seems paradoxical that birds should be well wrapped up in a highly efficient heat-retaining cover and at the same time require an equally efficient cooling system. Birds have no sweat glands. How then do they dispose of surplus heat? It seems that they get rid of it by means of the large air sacs which extend out from the lungs (already referred to in connection with breathing; see also page 58). It seems that air circulates freely in them. It has been estimated that in an average bird the volume of air sacs is about 20 per cent of the total volume of the bird (excluding feathers) and that in flight three times as much air is breathed in as is required for the supply of oxygen to the lungs. Birds, therefore, have an internal air-cooling system, or even a water-cooling system which is more efficient because it seems that the inner surface of the air sacs is moist and this moisture would evaporate in the circulating air, as sweat evaporates from your forehead in a breeze, and keeps you cool.

CHAPTER VI

Feathers

So FAR I have asked you to think about birds, and also I hope encouraged you to study them, as living objects. I referred to them in relation to their environments, how some of them are modified and adapted to fit into their various haunts and different ways of living. I mentioned also some of the simpler aspects of their behavior throughout the year. Now look more closely at the bird itself: what does it consist of in the way of feathers, flesh and bones, and how does it work? Feathers, for instance, provide a wealth of interesting information and the whole of this chapter will be devoted to them.

CONTOURS OF BIRDS

When we speak of the contours of a bird we mean much the same as when we refer to the contours of the countryside; they are the component parts which together give each their special shape. The way in which feathers give shape and character to a bird is illustrated very strikingly when the feathers are removed, as when a dead bird is plucked. The scraggy morsel which is revealed as the body of a robin, for instance, seems a ridiculous shadow of the splendid creature puffed out with importance which stands in command of our bird table.

In this photograph of a herring gull and its chicks, the adult shows the smooth contours and general streamlined appearance that is characteristic of birds. The herring gull is a successful and adaptable species that has been able to take advantage of man's activities. Nowadays many herring gulls get much of their food from the wastage of the fishing industry and from municipal garbage dumps. Compare this bird with the photographs of a herring gull in flight on page 39.

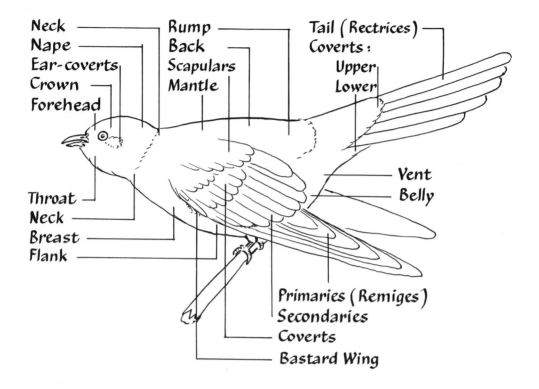

Neck
Nape
Ear-coverts
Crown
Forehead

Rump
Back
Scapulars
Mantle

Tail (Rectrices)
Coverts:
Upper
Lower

Vent
Belly

Throat
Neck
Breast
Flank

Primaries (Remiges)
Secondaries
Coverts
Bastard Wing

There are a number of fairly distinct features in bird contours. It is useful to become acquainted with their names, although those of you already experienced in field identification will be familiar with most, for they are referred to in the descriptions of birds, and their use has become more or less standardized. Several features have alternative names, like "ear-coverts" and "auriculars" and "moustache" and "malar region," but you will soon learn about them. A descriptive list of these features is much less instructive than a named illustration.

FEATHER STRUCTURE

What an amazingly complex object a feather is! It is well worthwhile to study it in detail. I am sure it is safe to say that everyone has handled feathers at some time or another, but I wonder how many have examined them really carefully. There are plenty of feathers available for study. Nature is prodigal in their production, providing every bird with at

least one new complete set each year. When you examine them, a magnifying glass will help to reveal structures not easily seen by the naked eye, and a microscope with fairly large magnification will bring into view even more interesting details.

General appearance

The commonest type of feather consists of two vanes supported by a long, tapering and fairly flexible central rod, usually known as the quill. The bottom part of the quill, the bare section, is called the calamus; when the feather is in place most of this section is embedded in the skin. There is a hole at the end of the calamus through which the growing feather is supplied with food and the pigments which color many so beautifully.

The upper part of the quill, where the vanes are attached, is called the shaft. At the junction of calamus and shaft there is sometimes an appendage called the after-shaft. It may be only a small tuft, or it may be quite large and have the appearance of a miniature feather, as in many of the game birds, like grouse and partridge. Less frequently, in primitive or degenerate birds like emu and cassowary, the aftershaft is as long as and nearly identical with the main part of the feather.

You will notice that the two vanes lie on opposite sides of the shaft, and that the shaft is grooved on the underside and smooth on the upperside. In many feathers, especially wing and tail feathers, the vanes are unbroken, like those of a leaf. When there are gaps or slits in the vanes, as in a feather which has been ruffed, you might think that permanent damage has been done. But this is not so. If you draw the slit portion between your fingers, from the shaft outwards, you will find that the breaks mend quite easily. Birds do this mending in their ruffled feathers when they preen; mending of feathers of course is only one of the objects served in preening.

Locking mechanism

How is it that gaps in vanes can be repaired in this way? When you pull the barbs between your fingers you are operating the very first type of zipper. The principle of the zipper was evolved in feathers long before it was "invented" by man. Unfortunately the mechanism is not visible to the naked eye and I will explain how it works, assisted by the diagrams in Fig. 9.

Each vane is made up of numerous straplike branches called barbs, which grow out from the shaft. Individual barbs are easily seen and can be separated from their companions. Each barb also has two rows of branches, called barbules. When you examine a section of the vane under magnification you will see that the barbules, like the barbs, do not grow straight out, but point forward, so that rows of facing barbules cross each other at right angles. Viewed from the upper or dorsal side of the feather, the distal barbules of one barb overlap the proximal ones of the next barb. (Distal means furthest away from the base of the feather and proximal nearest the base.)

The two sets of overlapping barbules have quite different features. Both are thin laminate (layered) structures, but with a number of differently shaped appendages. The ones I want you to note in particular are on the underside of the distal barbule which, you will remember, overlaps the proximal one. Some of these appendages, or barbicels, are hooked at the tip. The hooks clip over the upper edges of underlying barbules which are thickened and curled to provide a ledge

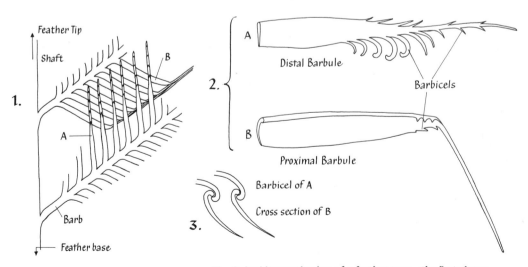

Fig. 9. Locking mechanism of a feather vane—the first zipper.

for them to grip on to. In this way adjacent barbules are locked together.

There is a certain amount of play in this ingenious snap-lock (which makes it superior to the man-made zipper) because of the criss-cross pattern of the barbules. You can demonstrate the elasticity quite easily if you grip a feather vane at two places a short distance apart and pull gently, as if intending to separate the barbs. The hooks of the upper barbule slide along the ledges of the lower one until they get to the sharp angle where they are held firmly. It requires a little bit of extra pull to get them off, when they do come off; that is, when a gap appears between the barbs of the vane.

KINDS OF FEATHERS

If you have plucked a fowl or other bird, or have seen one plucked, you will have noticed that there are different kinds of feathers. All have the same origin, but in the course of evolution there have been modifications for different purposes. It is interesting to make a small collection of the different kinds of feathers. The main types are usually classified as follows, but remember that because all feathers are fundamentally similar there are intermediates which are not easily assigned to any particular group.

Contour feathers

Contour feathers are those which contribute most to the outward appearance of birds. They possess a shaft, which is fairly stiff, vanes which for the most part have interlocking barbules and there is often an aftershaft. They are quite intricate in structure, as you will have realized from a study of their locking device, and they represent an advanced stage in feather development. Their main function is to provide a warm protective covering. In addition they form the basis for the colors which serve to distinguish one species from another. Some have become specialized as wing and tail feathers, the remiges and rectrices and their supporting coverts, which are essential for flight. Others

have been modified in various ways for special purposes, as in the emotional life of birds when certain tufts of feathers and other adornments are used in connection with courtship, both to attract the opposite sex and to repel rivals.

Plumules or semiplumes

In most contour feathers, sometimes called plumes, you will find that the basal part of the vanes are fluffy. The barbs are separate and they cannot be joined by pressing together, because the barbules do not have the interlocking mechanism. This open or plumose structure is typical of a group of feathers which are mainly small and which are tucked away under the contour feathers. They are called semiplumes or plumules, and intergrade with the very fluffy or plumose down feathers. The main function of these soft feathers is to fill up the spaces at the base of the contour feathers; they are the bird's warm underclothes.

One difficulty in classifying feathers by their appearance is the exceptions we come across. It is worth mentioning the case of owl's contour feathers which are very fluffy and might be identified as plumules. They have few interlocking barbules, except in the flight feathers, and even in these there are quite large areas of open barbs. Open-structured feathers and barbules with long filaments give owls their characteristically soft plumage. This feature is associated with their silent flight; a whitish colored barn owl flitting silently in the twilight, usually in search of small rodents, is indeed a ghostly object.

Down feathers

Plumules with relatively short shafts and long spidery barbs are generally classified as down. Downy feathers are found in many species. Sometimes they are packed in a felty mass under the contour feathers, as in cormorant and shag, but they are particularly associated with members of the duck family. Mention of down immediately brings to mind the name "eiderdown." As the name indicates this is properly the down of the eider duck, a common bird in northern coastal waters, but the name is used commercially to describe any bird down. The eider lines her nest with these soft feathers which are plucked from her body, and indeed are specially grown for this purpose. When the bird leaves the nest she pulls the down over the eggs, and as the down is mottled brown in color it conceals the white eggs from hungry predators.

Adult down has a shaft, sometimes very short, perhaps only a few millimeters in length, and it also has an aftershaft. In these respects it differs from nestling down, which is somewhat simpler in structure. It consists of a small root or calamus, capped with a bunch of long filamentous barbs.

Filoplumes

Another feather type is the hair-like filoplumes. These are not readily seen until the contour and down feathers are removed, and because of this many of you will make your first acquaintance with them, as I did, when you see your mother singeing "hairs" on a chicken which she is getting ready to cook. These hair-like feathers, often quite numerous, consist of a calamus and shaft and usually only a few short barbs at the tip. Their function seems to be rather a mystery. Perhaps they are all that remains of superfluous contour feathers whose numbers have become fewer as specialization increased.

Other types

One of the most interesting of the less common kinds of feather is powder-down. Powder-down occurs in patches, usually on the breast and abdomen, and notably on bittern and gray heron among British birds. It feels greasy to the touch, but this is because it is flaky in structure, like powdered graphite or, in coarser form, flaked naphthalene or soap flakes, any substance in fact in which the particles consist of thin flakes which readily slide on each other. In powder-

down the flakes are formed from the disintegrating horny covering of the barbs and barbules.

Another type of modified feather is found in the bristles which line the gape (wide-open mouth) of birds which catch insects on the wing, such as whip-poor-will, swift, swallow, and members of the numerous flycatcher family (*Muscicapidae*). If you get the chance to examine a dead specimen of one of these birds you should pry the mouth open wide. You will find the size of the opening surprisingly large in relation to the size of the bird, and you will see how the bristles extend the catching area. You can imagine that the presence of these side "fingers" must be a great help if the bird is not quite accurate in its attempt to catch an insect in its mouth (and it must be a difficult feat when both bird and insect are moving rapidly in the air).

FEATHER MOLT

I am sure you know that birds lose their feathers from time to time. Usually this is quite normal. Regular loss and replacement of outer skin or other covering is characteristic of most living things; in trees, for instance, the outer layer of bark peels off or wears away and is continually added to from the cambium layer between bark and wood; snakes shed their skins; dogs and cats leave hairs on mats and chair covers; even on our own skin there is constant abrasion and replacement of the outer layer of cells. Outer coverings protect, and as they are subjected to wear and tear they need constant replacement. In some cases, it is most practical that replacement should be by constant growth, as in our fingernails, and in others that the old coat should be completely discarded and replaced with a new one, as in birds.

It is interesting that birds cast their worn feathers, a few at a time and not all at once. The reason for this is obvious when we remember that the main function of feathers is to insulate the body against changes in temperature; most birds would not survive if left naked while the new coat grew. Important also is the fact that certain feathers are essential for flight and it would be a disaster for many of them to be grounded for any length of time. The molt of wing and tail feathers is so arranged that there is seldom more than one from each side missing at a time. An exception is found in the ducks, geese and swans which do molt flight feathers all at once, but in the vulnerable period they take evasive action; they become very secretive and hide away as much as possible from predators.

Sequence of plumages

Most of you have seen chicks of the domestic fowl, either alive or in pictures, especially on Easter cards, and know that they do not have feathers like their parents. They are fluffy little balls of down. Many of you also must have seen, towards the end of the breeding season, one bird feeding another of quite a different appearance, a robin, for instance, feeding a bird which did not have a red breast and was rather speckled in appearance. The simple rule is that birds have three main types of plumage during development, nestling, juvenile and adult.

Although the chick of the domestic fowl emerges from its egg well covered in a thick coat of fluffy down and can totter about on

its feet within an hour or two—not immediately, as often suggested in illustrations —the chicks of all birds do not hatch in this condition. Those of you who have been lucky enough to see into the nest of some bird, such as a catbird, when the young have just hatched, will have seen chicks which are quite helpless and practically naked; the downy coat grows later. Nestlings which are born helpless and are constantly brooded by their parents in their youngest days do not have the same need for a protective coat as nestlings which are able to run about almost as soon as they are hatched.

The nestling down is soon replaced by a second coat whose feathers more resemble in structure those of the adult, but which often have a different color pattern, sometimes very different, but in others only recognizable after a lot of experience. The feathers of this juvenile or fledgling plumage grow out from the same roots in the skin as did the down feathers; they behave in the way your adult teeth did when they replaced your milk teeth by pushing them out from underneath. Sometimes the down hangs on to the tip of the new feathers. You should look for them when you see a young bird; if you breed pigeons you will know them quite well, because they remain attached to the juvenile

The golden plover, like many other shorebirds, molts its body plumage twice a year, in early spring and again after the breeding season. The winter plumage lacks the black and white pattern in face and underparts which makes the bird so striking in appearance when it is in breeding plumage. Here both summer and winter plumages are shown. The juvenile plumage is very like that of the adult in winter.

feathers for a long time and give a hoary look to the ungainly fat squab.

As a rule the juvenile feathers appear quite soon in the young chick. They are easiest seen in those chicks which never have very much down. A point of interest to note is that they are not evenly distributed over the body, but are bunched together in various patches and tracts, which are technically called pterylae. The pattern is distinct for each species and can be examined in adult birds if the feathers are clipped instead of plucked.

In birds which are very dependent on flight, like the swallow and swift, it is important that the juvenile plumage should grow quickly and be fully formed so that the young birds can fly when they leave the nest. But in ground birds, like ducks, game birds and plovers, there is less urgency, and the chicks run about for some time before the juvenile coat is fully developed.

In many birds, especially the smaller kinds, · the juvenile plumage is molted after a few months. You are unlikely to see speckled robins, for instance, after August or early September, unless conditions have been favorable for very late broods. The brown plumage of young swans, called cygnets, is usually in evidence much longer, and so also is the juvenile dress of young gulls. The general rule is that there is an autumn molt of juvenile plumage and although in some birds the first adult dress is like all subsequent ones, except for some subtle differences visible to practiced eyes, in others the full adult plumage only appears after several annual molts.

It is also interesting to note that at the juvenile molt it is only the body feathers which are changed. The first set of wing and tail feathers are retained for they have scarcely been used and are still in good condition. Young birds are different in appearance in order that they may be better camouflaged at the time when they are most vulnerable, and it is enough to have a disruptive pattern on the body feathers only. Important also is the fact that growing new feathers puts quite a strain on a bird's constitution; those who keep pets will know that a molting bird is often rather sickly.

There are many more things to refer to in the fascinating story of feather molt (there is a whole book on the subject of molt in only one species) but I can only mention some of them very briefly and hope you will be interested to read other accounts and, best of all, to collect data from your own observations. If you are fortunate to have the chance to examine a recently dead bird—even one brought home from a meat market—with plumage intact, spend a little time examining the feathers carefully and note down various points of interest.

The important point to remember about feather molt is that in its simplest essentials it is a periodic removal of a protective covering which has become the worse for wear because of constant use. In the course of evolution, different birds have elaborated this theme in different ways. I have referred to some of them in the sequence of molt from nestling to adult, some having a very striking juvenile plumage and others, like the swallow, being the image of their parents when they leave the nest. Also to be considered are partial molts when males in particular change a few feathers here and there into some brighter color, resulting in a gayer dress with which to woo their mates or to strike fear into the hearts of rivals.

The only other general point I will bring to your notice is the sequence in which feathers are discarded in any particular molt. Again in its simplest beginnings one can imagine that all feathers were discarded together, in the way that a snake sheds its skin more or less all at once, but this has obvious disadvantages and birds have overcome the difficulty in various ways. Some birds start to discard their feathers at the head and work slowly towards the tail so that there are never any very obvious gaps; other species molt in the reverse direction; also tail feathers are usually replaced from the center pair outward and wing feathers from the junction of primaries and secondaries.

FEATHER COLORS

I think we would all agree that one of the most delightful things about birds is the bright colors of their plumage. I wonder how many would agree to colors being more attractive than songs and calls. It is a strange fact that some of the best songsters are shyest in their habits, keeping well hidden in the shrubbery, and also that many are less brightly colored than species whose voices do not weave the same magic spell. The obvious example which comes to mind is the nightingale, which, it is safe to say, is known to far more people by its voice than by the color of its feathers, even by its general appearance, for relatively few of those who have heard it have seen one. But appreciation of bird sounds is very individual and depends on various circumstances and associations. I, for example, get greater pleasure from hearing the call of a curlew or oystercatcher than from the song of a nightingale. Of course it is not very satisfactory trying to judge between the attractiveness of things which appeal to the ear and those which appeal to the eye. Many birds have to be seen pretty closely and in a good light to appreciate the fine points of their dress. A starling on a bare autumn tree silhouetted against a bright sky is a much less pleasing object than one on the lawn when, like a knight in burnished armor, the sun catches the iridescent purples and greens of its new and shiny silver-speckled feathers.

There is a great diversity of colors and color combinations sometimes giving ensembles which might shock those who have good taste in designing ladies' fashions but which seems quite suited to birds in their natural environments. A striking combination of bright golden yellow, red, black and white on a brown body is the unmistakable pattern of the European goldfinch, now an established resident on Long Island and other areas; it reminds one of a scholar in a woolen school sweater. The curious combination of colors in the male mandarin duck strikes a bizarre note on our ponds. Yellow is associated with the common gold-

finch, yellow warbler and yellowthroat. Red is a striking color in several species besides the robin. It is a richer color in the male painted bunting, is a distinctive patch on the crown of the redpoll and rump of the redstart, while the males of the crossbill, the scarlet tanager and the cardinal are almost wholly bright red.

What do these and all the other varied colors found in birds consist of? Colors on bird plumages are derived from two quite different sources. One is chemical pigments, which correspond with the various vegetable and mineral dyes used for coloring fabrics, and the other the refraction of light, similar to the colors on soap bubbles, a rainbow and the bevelled edge of a mirror. The latter has no substance, but depends on the fact that daylight is made up of a mixture of colors, the colors of the spectrum, and that it is broken up into its component parts when it passes through a prism. As this fact is sometimes difficult to grasp I may remind you of the simple experiment illustrating it in reverse; when the colors of the rainbow are painted on a disc which is then revolved at high speed the individual colors disappear and the disc looks white.

The chemical pigments are relatively few considering the variety of colors found in birds, but they intermingle in several ways to produce different effects. One effect is illustrated when a gauzy black dress is put over a red petticoat. The comparison is apt because the "gauzy black dress" corresponds with a group of pigments known by the general name melanin. Pure melanins give a limited range of dark colors from black to reddish-brown. The "red petticoat" would correspond to another group of colors of a different origin and chemical composition named by different authorities carotenoids and lipochromes. These compounds are the usual source of red and yellow colors. Various shades of red and yellow, reddish-brown, brown, gray, black and white account for most of the colors of northern birds. Green, purple and blue often belong to the iridescent or metallic group, whose colors are brought about by the refraction of light in the superficial layers of cells. A characteristic of iridescent colors is that they appear shiny or burnished and the color varies depending on the angle at which they are viewed. The patch of color, or speculum, like a distinctive badge or crest in the center of the wing of many species of duck, consists mainly of iridescent colors.

Pigments are sometimes thought to be the by-products of a bird's metabolism, or the chemical changes which take place in the normal course of being alive. They are carried to the feathers in the blood stream through the opening at the base of the quill. It may be noted here that white is due to a lack of pigment. In some species, gulls especially, it is the normal and characteristic color, but most species have a rare white phase in which either the color-producing mechanism fails to work or the pigments are not carried to their destination. This phenomenon and its proper name, albinism, will be familiar to most of you; albinos are found among animals also, such as white mice and certain breeds of white rabbit in which the eyes are a faded pink color, and even in the human species. There are few localities in which there does not occur from time to time, for example, a white or partially white blackbird, sparrow or robin. If you proceed to advanced studies in biology you will learn about the mechanism of inheritance which explains this unusual condition. Along with albinism there is melanism which, as the word suggests, is an excess of black pigment in the normal color, and erythrism (excess of red) and xanthochroism (excess of yellow).

Blue-winged teal.

CHAPTER VII

Collecting and Digesting Food

BEAKS, OR BILLS, like feathers, are an important part of the external features of birds, but they also have a close connection with their internal anatomy. They are at the receiving end of the long tube into which food disappears. This route, and its side lanes, is called the digestive system or alimentary system, or just plainly, food canal. The structure of certain parts of the food canal is determined by the kind of food it has to deal with, and the food offered to it is largely determined by beak shapes. Beak shapes and food canal, therefore, are an important subject for this chapter.

BEAK SHAPES

You will remember when referring to feather modification I mentioned some birds, like swallow, swift and whip-poor-will, which can open their mouths very wide and scoop up insects in the air by flying at them like living butterfly nets. Birds which use this method exclusively have little or no use for beaks in the actual collection of food. There is a general rule in biology, as you may know, that a part of the body not used tends to dwindle in size and even disappear, and in the birds mentioned beaks are very insignificant (Fig. 11).

Other birds besides the weak-billed "scoopers" take insects on the wing. Members of the large flycatcher family, like yellow-bellied flycatcher and eastern phoebe, catch insects by snapping at them and their beaks are wide and flat. You can always identify a true flycatcher by its compressed beak, as if it had been squashed, and the presence of bristles at the edge of the mouth. But there is no uniformity in this bill pattern in birds which catch insects in flight for the gaily colored bee-eater of Europe also hawks for them and it has a long sharp bill, though slightly flattened.

The black swift, like others of its family, has a very small beak and a wide mouth. This type of beak and mouth is found in many different kinds of birds that feed on small or soft-bodied insects caught in flight.

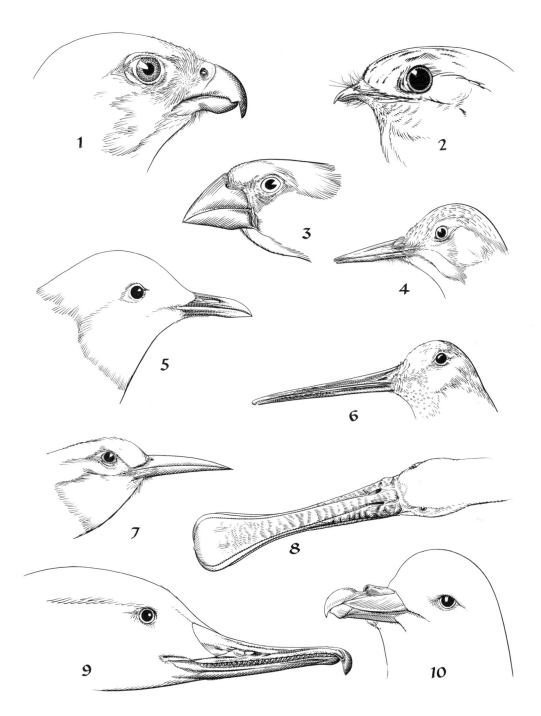

Fig. 10. Beaks for different ways of feeding. (1) Peregrine falcon. (2) Whip-poor-will. (3) Finch. (4) Woodpecker. (5) Black-headed gull. (6) Woodcock. (7) Bee-eater. (8) Spoonbill. (9) Merganser. (10) Fulmar.

The beaks of puffins serve both for catching and holding small, slippery fish, such as sand eels, and also as organs of display. In early spring a brightly colored outer covering grows over the beak. This greatly increases its size and brilliance and is shed after the breeding season is over. This photograph shows a pair of horned puffins, so called from the erect horn-like protuberance over the eye, in full breeding finery.

It is not unusual to see an English sparrow fluttering about and snapping at insects, with what success it is difficult to say, but sparrows are essentially seed-eaters and their bills are specially adapted to deal with that kind of food. Most seeds are encased in various layers of less digestible materials, as you will know if you have tried to extract the grain from an ear of wheat, and the bills of seed-eaters have special sharp edges for cutting these away. For breaking open harder shelled seeds the beaks are strengthened; they are usually short and thick or conical-shaped.

The seed-eaters include buntings, finches and grosbeaks. One of the shyest woodland finches in England, the hawfinch, has a powerful bill. It is strong enough to crack open cherry pits, which is no mean feat. It has been estimated that the pressure required is about 100 lbs. and in order to stand the strain the inside of the mouth is fortified with large horny pads. It is hard to believe that a small bird could have a beak nearly as strong as the head of a pair of pliers. This modification of the hawfinch beak is a good illustration of how competition for survival drives birds to look for unusual sources of food.

English sparrow and field sparrow are fairly alike in general appearance but the field sparrow can be distinguished at once by its pinkish slender beak; it is not conical-shaped as in the others. The field sparrow lives on soft food when insects, grubs and larvae are available, but in the winter months it does take seeds, although these are apparently dealt with by the gizzard rather than by the beak. In another very large group, the warblers, beaks are almost invariably slender. Warblers usually take what insects they can find readily available in exposed places, and when cold weather comes to temperate regions they move further south where insects are plentiful. They do not dig for grubs as woodpeckers do, hacking into timber for the larvae of wood-boring insects. For this purpose woodpeckers are equipped with chisel-shaped bills; they are straight, hard and sharp.

The turnstone has a beak like that of a woodpecker, but it is used for turning over and probing under stones on the seashore. Other members of the large group of waders, to which the turnstone belongs, get most of their food in soft places, like sandy beaches, mud flats and marshes. The worms, small crustacea and other items on their "bill of fare" are often below the surface, and the birds have to dig for them. Consequently their beaks are long and probe-shaped. The extraordinary long beaks of woodcock and curlew are good examples.

Other feeders on the soft margins of coastal and inland waters are members of the duck family. Most ducks make sieves of their broad flat beaks. They take in mouthfuls of muddy water and strain it through the edge of the beak, which is provided with rows of bristles, like the teeth of a comb. The edible particles are sorted out in the mouth. These serrations along the edge of the mouth of ducks and other birds are not teeth, but horny projections from the lining of the mouth. Horny projections which look more like teeth are found in the beaks of a special group of ducks represented by such divers as the merganser, sometimes known as "sawbills." In these birds the beak is narrow and the "teeth" are used for gripping fish. Not all the fish eaters have this type of beak as you will see if you examine, for example, those of kingfisher, puffin, gannet and cormorant.

The spoonbills take their name from their odd-looking spatulate beaks. When feeding, the bird sweeps its bill from side to side in shallow water. The bill is held somewhat open and closes at once on anything edible that is swept between the mandibles. Most species of spoonbills, like these Australian royal spoonbills, are white in color but the roseate spoonbill, which inhabits the southern U.S. and Central and South America, has beautiful pink and crimson plumage. The spoonbills are closely related to the ibises in spite of their very different beaks.

Australian Jabiru storks. Storks typically feed in marshes or damp, low-lying fields. They have long, sharp, heavy bills with which they catch and kill frogs, snakes and small mammals as well as smaller prey such as insects.

A final word about the carnivores of the bird world, the birds of prey, like golden eagle, buzzard and peregrine falcon, and of course the nocturnal hunters, the owls. You will remember that a feature of a carnivore mouth is the long pointed canine teeth, sometimes called eyeteeth, whose function is to tear up food. In birds, the canine teeth are represented by a single feature, the hooked tip of the beak. It is a most effective instrument, as you will agree if you watch a bird of prey in a zoo if not in the wild, efficiently tearing apart a large piece of meat.

These are some examples of beak shapes and the types of food for which they are suited. I suggest when you see a bird, either alive, stuffed or in an illustration, you pay particular attention to the shape of its beak and try to find out what kind of food it lives on. This could become a detailed study of fascinating interest. For example, in order to avoid competition, some birds tend to be specialized feeders. This was brought out in a recent study of the food of two species of flamingo which had the same feeding grounds but whose beaks were equipped to take different items.

FOOD CANAL

Even the most casual observer will have noticed that although a bird may test a morsel of food with its bill, or carry it in its mouth, when it has decided to swallow it, it gulps the food down. It could not chew food in the way a mammal does, for birds have no teeth, at least in the conventional meaning of teeth.

All birds have tongues—you can see a robin's quite plainly when it is singing—and they vary a lot in shape depending on how they are used. One worth noting in particular is the tongue of many of the woodpeckers. It is of very great length and is used for probing amazing distances into nooks, crannies and crevices for ants, grubs and other insects which are caught on the sticky tip of the tongue. The hairy woodpecker's tongue is so long that its roots are coiled up at the back of its head. If you ever get the chance of handling a dead specimen you should take

the opportunity to dissect the tongue, and also examine the structure of the tongue in other birds. One other point about bird tongues is that, compared with ours for example, they have relatively few taste "buds" or groups of cells whose function is to record the sense of taste. It seems to be generally agreed that birds have little sense of taste, possibly because they bolt their food and have other means of testing its edibility.

Food disappears from the mouth through the pharynx into the gullet or esophagus, which leads into the stomach: I will use the word stomach in the meantime, but will explain presently that a bird's stomach is somewhat different from ours. Sometimes food passes more or less directly to the stomach, as in most insectivorous birds, for example. But in other birds, especially those which live on seeds and grain, food is stored temporarily in a sack-like structure called the crop. This is an expanded part of the gullet. From the crop, food is supplied to the stomach as required. Domestic fowl and pigeons, for instance, have a crop, which you can feel quite easily when it is packed with corn.

A typical bird stomach consists of two parts. First, there is a section called the proventriculus which leads into the second part called the gizzard. The proventriculus supplies various digestive juices which help to break down the seeds and grain and other hard items; the gizzard is a muscular structure which pounds them up. In some ways the combined action is similar to what happens to the food in our mouth when the salivary glands supply juices and the teeth break the food up, making it easier for the stomach to perform digestion. In some birds (the English sparrow for instance) which take very hard seeds, the gizzard is assisted in the grinding process with suitably sized grains of sand or grit which are swallowed for this purpose. The ostrich also has this kind of gizzard; being a much bigger bird it swallows quite large stones, even nails and other curious objects which may be available. This habit was to the disadvantage of ostriches in certain parts of South Africa at one

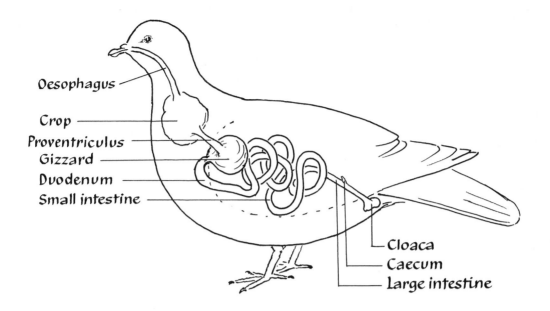

Oesophagus
Crop
Proventriculus
Gizzard
Duodenum
Small intestine

Cloaca
Caecum
Large intestine

time because many were slaughtered to see if the stomach contained diamonds, surely one of the most unusual methods of prospecting. When soft food is the main diet, the gizzard is less well developed. You should remember that these important sections of the food canal, crop, proventriculus and gizzard, vary a good deal from one species to another depending on the kind of food supplied by the beak, and even in one bird when there is a change of diet during its development and from one season to another.

Before describing the next section in the food canal I should mention an interesting and rather unusual practice of some birds, mainly birds of prey, including owls, which get rid of indigestible parts of their food by ejecting them from the mouth, instead of letting them continue in the food canal to be disposed of as faeces. The fur, feather and bones of the mammals, birds and other animals which form the diet of these birds are swallowed along with the parts which can be digested, but they remain in the proventriculus and are compacted into a hard pellet which is eventually cast out through the mouth. If you know where a barn owl or

any other bird of prey is in the habit of roosting it is almost certain that you will find pellets underneath. Pellets are frequently examined by investigators to find out what these various pellet-forming species live on.

The macerated food partly acted on by digestive juices in the stomach passes into the small intestine whose function is to complete digestion. This means a further breaking down of the main food elements, mainly carbohydrates, fats and proteins, into substances which are readily absorbed into the blood stream. In the first part of the intestine, the duodenum, the food is attacked by certain elements, called enzymes, which are provided by the pancreas. Bile is also provided by the liver, either directly or from its storage container, the gall bladder. Some birds do not have a gall bladder. The small intestine is usually a very long tube coiled up inside the abdomen. Any material left undigested or not absorbed passes into the large intestine, usually a much shorter tube. In the widened extremity of this tube, the cloaca, the waste material is collected and finally ejected along with urine from the kidney.

CHAPTER VIII

Lungs and Heart

IN THE FOOD CANAL the substances required by the body are extracted and used both for building up tissues and for producing energy so that the muscles can function. For the production of energy, certain food substances have to be combined with oxygen, like the union of oxygen with carbon in a fire provides energy to boil a kettle. Where does the oxygen come from and how does it and the substances with which it combines get to the places where they are required? The answer to this question is found in a study of the lungs and heart and their associated structures.

LUNGS

Oxygen is obtained of course from the air, and as birds breathe they extract this element from it into their lungs. Unlike the food canal, the air passages form a closed system. That is to say, they are connected to the outside by only one opening, whereas in the food canal there is an entrance and an exit, the mouth and anus. Air can go in at two places for, like us, birds can breathe through their mouth as well as nose, except certain birds like gannet and cormorant whose nose is sealed, an adaptation related to their habit of diving into the sea for fish.

The external openings of the nose, or external nares, are clearly seen near the base of the upper mandible, or in the cere in certain birds, like pigeons, which have this swollen fleshy part at the base of the beak. They are connected with slit-like openings on the roof of the mouth near the pharynx, or beginning of the food canal. When you look into the mouth of a bird the large aperture you see at the back is the pharynx; the opening into the windpipe or trachea is less noticeable, for it is a long slit at the root of the tongue. This opening, the glottis, can be tightly shut by strong muscles to prevent food from "going down the wrong way." In the trachea just beyond the glottis is the larynx which corresponds with our larynx, or "Adam's apple," but in birds it is not used for producing sounds. Bird voices have their origin at the other end of the long tubular trachea in a unique structure appropriately called syrinx after the pipes of the mythical god, Pan.

The syrinx is a modification of the trachea tube where it divides into two branches, the bronchi, one leading to each lung. The lungs are a mass of tubes, smaller ones branching out from larger ones, but, unlike the branches of a tree and the branches of the human lung, the small tubes join up with one another (or anastomose), and apparently air circulates rather than ebbs and flows. So far as I know the exact route of circulation and the way in which continuous movement in one direction comes about is not fully understood.

One curious feature of the air passages is the enormous sacs which grow out from various places in the lung tubes, like balloon distensions from a bicycle tube when there is a crack in the tire. One of the biggest of these air sacs, the abdominal (or rather abdominal pair, for most are paired), is a continuation of the bronchus or main stem of the lung. Others arise from definite points in the lung system and lie in various parts of the body cavity, and even penetrate into a number of bones. The next time there is chicken for dinner, examine the main wing bone or humerus. When you break it open you will find that it is hollow whereas the similar bone in a rabbit, for example, would be filled with marrow. Also, when out walking, keep a lookout for bird skeletons and examine them to see which bones are pneumatic and which are not; a good place to find them is among the tidal debris of the seashore. There is an easy way to spot the hollow ones, which are whiter and cleaner and less greasy looking. Remember that the pneumatic bones contained part of the air sacs which are extensions from the bird's lungs. This fact is emphasized by the statement often made, which seems credible enough though I have no first-hand knowledge of it, that a bird with a broken humerus cannot easily be asphyxiated by throttling because it can continue to take air into its lungs through the ruptured air sac in the bone; in other words it can breathe through its broken wing.

I have explained that the lungs of birds consist essentially of a lot of interconnected tubes in which the air apparently circulates, rather than a many-branched tree of tubes in which air would ebb and flow when the lungs are compressed and expanded, as they are when we breathe out and in. Birds breathe in a quite different way from us. The lungs are not compressed and expanded —they remain immovable. Air is forced through them, and it seems certain that the air sacs play an important part in bringing this about. If you watch a bird at rest, especially just after it has landed from flying, you will often see the abdomen going in and out rhythmically, like the chest of a person who has just been running. Pressure on the air sacs would force air through the lung tubes. In flight, the bellows action seems to be brought about by the compression and expansion of the chest cage formed by the ribs and sternum. There is experimental proof that breathing in flight is synchronized with the wing beats.

I will mention very briefly how important these features are to a bird. When we run we have to breathe harder; the breathing muscles increase their demand for oxygen as well as the running muscles. In birds, only the flying muscles increase their oxygen requirements, for the faster they fly the faster they pump air through the lungs: within reason a bird cannot readily run out of breath. Another very important point is the relatively great amount of air in the air passages. Air circulates in the lung tubes, possibly only in one direction. This means that the absorptive surfaces of the lungs where oxygen is extracted by a mesh of fine blood vessels, are continually supplied with fresh air fully charged with oxygen when the bird is breathing out as well as breathing in. The only comparison I can think of is a double-action pump in which a constant stream of water is maintained by both up-stroke and down-stroke; our lungs are like single-action pumps, supplying fresh air on the in-stroke and getting rid of used air on the out-stroke.

You will see, therefore, that the method evolved by birds for supplying oxygen to their "fires" is highly efficient and is consistent with the fact that they consume a relatively great amount of fuel. It has been calculated that some birds can consume as much as twice their own weight in food in a day and most of what is eaten is usable food with very little "roughage." Birds are like racing cars—they have a tremendous amount of energy for their size, quick starting powers, high speeds and high fuel consumption.

BLOOD CIRCULATION

I have just compared birds with racing cars and I apologize for continuing this rather mechanical analogy, but I can think of

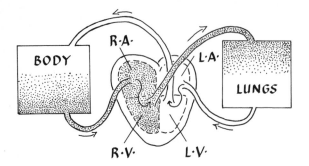

Fig. 12. Diagram of blood circulation. The left ventricle (L.V.) pumps blood carrying oxygen and food along arteries to the body. The waste products of combustion making "impure" blood (shaded parts) are carried back along veins to the right auricle (R.A.). This blood is transferred to another pump, the right ventricle (R.V.), which sends it to the lungs to discharge waste gas, carbon dioxide and to collect another supply of oxygen. The "pure" blood then returns to the left auricle (L.A.).

nothing better. A powerful engine and a plentiful supply of high octane fuel in the tank would be of little use without an efficient means of bringing them together. Good carburation is necessary, and in birds the fuel supply system is the blood and its circulation. It carries both food from the absorptive linings of the small intestine, which is filtered in the liver on the way, and oxygen from the vascular areas of the lungs, by means of the hemoglobin, to the tissues where combustion is required; it carries away the waste products of combustion, the carbon dioxide, back to the lungs where it is exhaled, and also the nitrogenous waste to the kidneys where it is disposed of in the urine.

If you have held a bird in your hand (and it is pleasant to do if the bird is not distressed), you will have noticed two things in particular. One is that the heart beats very quickly, even although you are certain the bird is not frightened. Birds' hearts normally beat much faster than ours. This is evidence of the high metabolism, the high rate of living and high fuel consumption I have referred to. Blood circulates through arteries and veins quicker than ours does and of course very much quicker than in the lower animals, most of which are normally sluggish in their movements. Our heart beats are usually around about 80-90 per minute, whereas a usual rate of heartbeat for a bird at rest is about 120 per minute, and at least double that when in flight. The pump which keeps up this pressure is, of course, the heart; in birds this organ is relatively large and the tubes

leading from it much stronger than in mammals of comparable size.

There are two important elements connected with this high rate of circulation. One is that birds, like mammals but not the lower animals, have a four-chambered heart and, in consequence, two independent circulations, I think you will find it easiest to comprehend what happens in this way. There are two chambers on each side of the heart. One on the left side, the left ventricle, pumps blood, carrying supplies of food and oxygen, through the arteries into all parts of the body, except the lungs, and back again through the veins, now charged with "exhaust" wastes into the reception chamber on the right side of the heart, the right auricle. This "used" blood is then transferred to the second pump, the right ventricle, which drives it to the lungs where it discharges its carbon dioxide, receives a fresh supply of oxygen and returns fresh into the other reception chamber, the left auricle, and then again, to complete the double circuit, into the first pump, the left ventricle. The other important point about the blood of birds is that it contains a very high proportion of red blood corpuscles, which means that volume for volume with our blood, for example, it carries a greater amount of oxygen (Fig. 12).

The second thing you will have noticed if you have had a bird in your hands is that it feels warm; even if you have only had a pet budgerigar perched on your finger you will have noticed how warm its feet are. It is said that certain Chinese made use of this characteristic of birds and in cold weather instead of wearing gloves or carrying a muff they carried a quail in their hands under the folds of their long sleeves. The normal temperature of most birds is higher than ours, which as you know averages about 98.6 degrees Fahrenheit. In most birds it is usually over 100 degrees, frequently as high as 110 degrees and even up to 115 degrees or more. Remember that bath water at 115 degrees will burn you. These temperatures are another indication that in birds "the fires of life burn brightly"—that there is a rapid consumption of fuel, that they live very intensely, that their metabolism is high.

A brood of young herons.

CHAPTER IX

Other Anatomical Features

MUSCLES

MUSCLES do all the work. They are the "engines" which are driven by the energy obtained from the combustion of food-fuel and oxygen. They puff out the feathers of the robin as it stands for a moment at the edge of the bird table on a cold day; there is a battery of these muscles, each very small, at the roots of the feathers. Muscles flap the wings of the mute swan which lift its 25-lb. weight with noisy beats from a long stretch of open water; they keep the heart going; they grind the corn in the gizzard and push food at the right speed and in the right direction along the tortuous coils of the intestines. There are many of them. I think it will be sufficient here to mention only those which are primarily connected with flight.

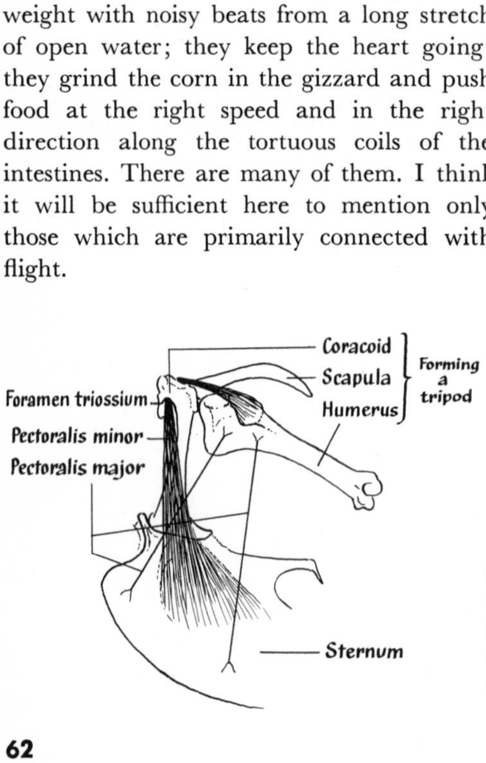

The flight muscles form the breast, which is the main edible part of table birds. It is interesting to note in passing that the breasts of some fowl are not very "meaty," and also that there is relatively less breast on a chicken than on a duck or goose. This is not necessarily due to lack of feeding but to the fact that chickens rarely use their flight muscles; sometimes they are never given the opportunity, as when they are kept in a battery, and, as I said before, disuse leads to atrophy. In a chicken the weight of the breast muscles is about one-twelfth of the total weight of the bird, whereas in a pigeon, a powerful flier, it amounts to nearly one-half.

What do the breast muscles consist of and how do they function? When a roasted table bird is being carved you will see that the breast is formed of two large muscles. They can be separated quite easily. One lies on top of the other, the outer being the major pectoral muscle, and the other the minor pectoral. Major is larger and its function is to pull the wing down, the important stroke, both keeping the bird in the air against the

Fig. 13. How breast muscles flap a wing. The wing, represented by its first bone—the humerus—is lifted by the contraction of the pectoralis minor, acting through the pulley of the foramen triossium. It is pulled down by the contraction of the pectoralis major (represented by two lines).

The Canada goose is a large, heavy-bodied bird, but thanks to its strong flight muscles it is capable of fast and long-sustained flapping flight. This individual has just been banded and released. The band can be seen on its left leg, which is held up under the tail, the position in which most birds except the passerines usually hold their legs when in flight.

force of gravity and propelling it forward. Minor lifts the wing in preparation for the down stroke, a movement which naturally requires much less energy.

Major is located, as you will see, on the underside of the wing and therefore in the most convenient position to get a direct pull on it so as to bring it down. In order to do this the muscle is attached to the underside of the first wing bone, the humerus. But minor also is on the underside of the wing and you may wonder how it can pull the wing up when any direct action would achieve the same effect as major. The way minor works is by a simple but ingenious device which illustrates a mechanical principle now well known in engineering, but which you would hardly expect to find in a bird. The muscle extends into a rope-like tendon which passes through an opening formed at the junction of three bones and then swings around and attaches to the upper side of the humerus. The three bones, clavicle, coracoid and scapular, form a tripod and the opening at their junction, the foramen triossium, acts like the wheel of a pulley. Contraction of minor exercises a pull on the "rope" passing over the "pulley" which converts the downward pull to an upward one. Engineers have a similar contrivance which you may have seen in use, for example, for lifting timber on to a truck or laying pipes in a drain.

SKELETON

The skeleton is the bony framework which holds the other parts of the body together. It is more compact and rigid than in most animals. Many bones are fused together, especially in the region of the pelvic girdle which has to be strong enough to take the shock of a landing bird. Other bones are joined with strong ligaments, some of which are quite flexible.

I mentioned in an earlier chapter some of the important features of bird skeletons connected with their adaptations for flight. All I propose to do here is to name the most important ones and to give a few hints on how some can be identified. This should be of special interest because bones are often discovered on country walks, especially among the high tide debris on the seashore, and one can learn a lot by trying to find out if they are bird bones, which bone it is and perhaps which bird it belonged to.

The easiest way to learn the names of the main bones of a bird's skeleton is by means of an illustration and Fig. 14 serves this purpose. It is always possible to distinguish the skull of a bird, and also of a mammal (unless it is very much broken up), by the presence of the large cavity which contained the brain. There is an opening into this space at the back of the head where the brain was

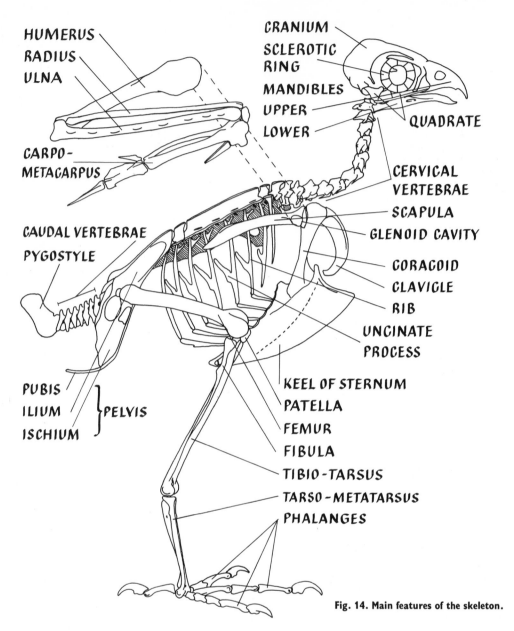

HUMERUS
RADIUS
ULNA

CARPO-
METACARPUS

CAUDAL VERTEBRAE
PYGOSTYLE

PUBIS
ILIUM } PELVIS
ISCHIUM

CRANIUM
SCLEROTIC
RING
MANDIBLES
UPPER
LOWER
QUADRATE

CERVICAL
VERTEBRAE
SCAPULA
GLENOID CAVITY
CORACOID
CLAVICLE
RIB
UNCINATE
PROCESS

KEEL OF STERNUM
PATELLA
FEMUR
FIBULA
TIBIO-TARSUS
TARSO-METATARSUS
PHALANGES

Fig. 14. Main features of the skeleton.

connected with the spinal cord. I mention this point because sometimes part of the pelvic girdle of a bird's skeleton is mistaken for a mammal skull. It does bear some resemblance, even to the extent of having what appear to be teeth sockets, but it never does have a cavity.

The front end of the skull usually ends in a sharp point which is sometimes hooked. The eye sockets or orbits are very large, enormous in owls, for the sense of sight is highly developed (see page 66). Sometimes one eye socket connects with the other through the skull, or at most they are divided by a thin sheet of bone called a septum. At the back of the skull and above the brain opening there is a projection or condyle, which connects with the first vertebra of the spinal column. In a mammal skull there are two condyles, one on each side of the brain opening, and of course there are teeth, or sockets where teeth had been.

The trunk of a bird's skeleton hangs together very well. The breastbone or sternum, which is quite small and insignificant in mammals, is very large and deeply keeled; a sternum looks like the hull of a yacht. Many of the ribs are in two sections and the parts connected with the backbone overlap each other by means of a backward projection called an uncinate process; this helps to protect the lungs which lie immediately under the ribs. The clavicles often fuse to form the well-known feature in a bird, the "wishbone" or furculum. The scapula or shoulder blade is like the short and broad sword we often see illustrated in the hands of Roman soldiers.

A number of bones are fused together to form the large pelvic girdle, the part sometimes mistaken for a mammal skull. Some of the vertebrae can be distinguished in the middle of it. A fairly large socket on each, which looks as if it might have contained an eye, holds the ball-like head of the femur, the first leg bone. The femur can always be distinguished from other leg bones by its rounded head. The second leg bone, the tibiotarsus, has a wheel-like distal end where it is jointed with the tarsometatarsus, commonly abbreviated to tarsus.

GONADS AND KIDNEYS

The important anatomical features essential for reproduction collectively are known as reproductive organs or gonads, and the essential parts are testes in the male and ovaries in the female. The gonads and the ducts by which their products are discharged are closely associated with the kidneys and their ducts, and are often referred to together as the urogenital system.

If you are interested in anatomy I suggest that you open up the abdomen of a newly dead bird and try to distinguish gonads and kidneys. In opening the abdomen be careful to cut only the thin wall; cut it longitudinally and then across, so that you can lift or push aside the coils of the intestines. The gonads and kidneys are fairly well up in the cavity and close to the backbone. The kidneys are long lobed objects, dark colored and spongy in texture. Near the top end of them, the end nearest the head, you will find the gonads. If the bird is adult, and if it is anywhere near the breeding season, there will be no difficulty in identifying the sex organs. In the male the two testes stand out quite clearly as whitish firm objects; in the nonbreeding season they will be smaller and flaccid.

The ovary of the female is quite different. It is clearly granular, perhaps like a miniature bunch of grapes, but as each "grape" represents a possible egg they will vary considerably in size, especially near the breeding season. An important point about the ovary is that there is only one usually on the bird's left side, although when well developed it may look central. In a very young female the ovary often is not easily found. At the rear end of the ovary (or testis) and kidney, you should be able to make out the ducts that lead from each to the end of the rectum near the anus. The duct from the ovary, the oviduct, is quite large, especially in a bird that has laid eggs. The duct from the testis, the vas deferens, is a thin wavy tube. The duct from the kidney, the ureter, is thin and more or less straight.

A word now on how testes and ovaries function. Testes manufacture sperms—short for "spermatozoa"—but the way they do this would take too long to explain here. All I need say is that sperms are special kinds of free-living cells (male) whose one and only purpose is to get away from the testis and join forces with cells of another kind (female) manufactured by the ovary. Nature is sometimes very prodigal and during the act of copulation, when the cock bird stands on the back of the hen and their cloacas are brought together, a great quantity of sperms are injected into the female oviduct. Only one sperm is required to fertilize an ovum. Each ovum leaves the ovary to wend its way down the oviduct, where it meets a sperm, is wrapped up in various membranes and a hard shell, and finally delivered as an egg into the nest.

EYES AND EARS

Birds, like humans, have five senses: feeling, taste, smell, hearing and sight; as you know we rely entirely on our senses for every kind of information about our surroundings. Feeling, taste and smell are relatively unimportant to birds which live so much of their life in the air. Feeling is vital to a mole living underground where it is too dark to see anything; smell and hearing are very important to a fox which moves about in undergrowth and often at night. I am sure you must have noticed how a dog, a near relative of the fox, temporarily out of touch with its master usually finds him again by listening and smelling although the master may be, to us, quite easy to see. Birds, on the other hand, could not perform the tricky feats of landing on twigs or telegraph wires, or indeed land anywhere in safety unless they had good eyesight.

Interesting proof of a bird's lack of smell was obtained in a recent experiment on herring gulls. The birds did not detect the presence of slightly rotten fish wrapped in thin paper and placed where they had learned to expect food. The packages remained untouched even when put among unwrapped fish which was quickly gobbled up. There are, however, a few birds, among them the turkey vulture, which do have a good sense of smell. I have already mentioned that birds' tongues have relatively few taste buds, or nerve centers whose function is to record taste, and you may wonder, as I do, how a bird selects what to eat. There is some evidence that it learns quickly to know by sight what is edible and possibly also there is a little bit of initial testing with bill and tongue—feeling and tasting.

Sight and hearing, especially the latter, are the senses on which birds almost wholly rely. A short introductory note on the anatomy of eyes and ears will help you to understand how they function. Anatomical evidence of the importance of eyes is found in at least two striking features, the relatively great size of the eyes and also of the part of the brain, the optic lobes, which deals with the sensations recorded by them. If you remove the top of the skull of a fresh specimen you will see the rounded projections of the optic lobes on each side of the brain.

A feature of birds' skulls is the great size of the cavities required for the eyes. In the live bird, the visible part of the eye is not always a reliable index of eye size for, like the iceberg, much of it is hidden beneath the surface. An impressive comparison is that the eye of the larger owls is about as large as the human eye, although the shapes are rather different. The essential feature in the structure of the eye is that there are outer and inner chambers filled with fluid and between them a transparent lens, like a magnifying glass. This lens is partly covered by an opaque iris with an opening in the center, the pupil, which can be varied in size. The pupil is the opening through which enters the view of whatever the eye is directed at. The image is recorded on the sensitive screen, the retina, at the back of the inner chamber.

It will help in the understanding of bird vision if you think for a moment of your own. With one eye you can focus your attention on a particular point and at the same time be aware of things in quite a wide area around it. Each eye, therefore, has two kinds of vision, "concentrated" and "general." The value of the second eye looking in the same direction is to give you another "bearing" on the focal point, which your brain converts into an appreciation of relative distances. We think of this as pretty efficient eyesight. Owls and some birds of prey have eyes directed forward like ours. Most birds, however, have eyes that look more or less in opposite directions, an arrangement that, surprisingly, is much more efficient than ours! I will try to show how this is so in as few words as possible. In the first place each eye has a separate range of "general" vision and with both in operation they cover a very wide field. A bird, therefore, has more area in its field of view than we have, and that can be very important for keeping a lookout for enemies. Another point is that each eye has separate "concentrated" vision,

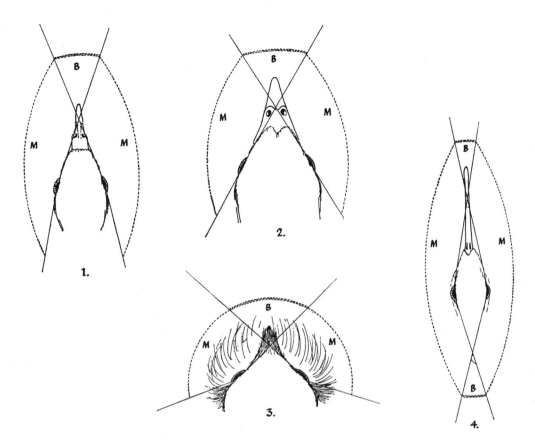

Fig. 15. Range of vision in various birds. Single dotted line monocular (M) vision, double lines binocular (B) vision. (1) Pigeon. (2) Golden eagle. (3) Snowy owl. (4) Woodcock. (N.B. Angles are only approximate.)

monocular vision, and it seems also that many (if not all) birds have a combined forward concentrated vision, binocular, like ours. Incredible as it may seem, a few birds, the woodcock in particular, have their eyes placed in such a way that they have backward binocular vision as well as forward. These points I hope will give you some food for thought and make you want to learn more about this fascinating subject.

A curious thing about the head of a bird is that there is no sign of ears. The tufts of feathers present on the heads of the long-eared and short-eared owls do not correspond with the external appendages of mammals whose purpose is to concentrate sounds into the hearing part of the ear. The opening into this is hidden under a group of special feathers, the auriculars, and sometimes it is quite large, as in owls whose sense of hearing is believed to be very acute. Stretched across the ear channel is the eardrum or tympanum, which, like ours, is vibrated by sound waves. The vibrations are transferred by means of a long thin bone, the columella, to the inner ear where nerves receive them and send them on to the brain. Experiments have shown that although some birds have an acute sense of sound, the range of scale they are sensitive to is more limited than ours. This means, for example, that birds with high-pitched voices probably do not hear very low notes; for example, the lower limit of hearing in the English sparrow is about 675 cycles per second and in the pheasant about 250 cycles per second.

CHAPTER X

Variation and Evolution

PEOPLE who are interested in natural history, and especially in bird biology, are almost certain to meet, sooner or later, the troublesome person who will pose the riddle, "Which came first, the hen or the egg?" Whether or not we may think this a silly question it shows that there is interest in evolution and most inquirers genuinely want to discuss the subject, even though we may find it difficult to answer one single question. Perhaps the contents of this chapter will put you in a favorable position to cope with your ordeal when it comes.

In its simplest terms, evolution means changes which appear during the course of time. An easy way to understand such changes is to study differences between birds. It is necessary to say in this context that the term "course of time" means time measured in millions of years and "present time" covers a long period, for although evolution is a continuous process its pace is exceedingly slow, and changes which can be measured are rarely visible in the lifetime of one person.

What present-day differences are there to study? In what way do birds vary? It is true to say, though you may find it hard to believe, that no two birds, even out of the same nest, are exactly alike, unless they are identical twins, and so far as I know there is no record of identical bird twins. Double-yolked eggs do occur, but I believe the yolks are usually two separate ova. Therefore if the chicks hatched successfully, and the chances are very much against their doing so, they would be like any other two chicks hatched from separate eggs.

There are of course a number of obvious differences, like those between males and females, between young birds and old birds, and seasonal changes, like the summer and winter plumages of ptarmigan and snow bunting and the bright dresses which many birds have in the breeding season. But even allowing for these, there are other ways in which birds differ. Not all English sparrows of similar sex and age, for example, are alike. If you really get to know the individuals of a small group of birds, as do people who make an intensive study of a small population, you will find them as unlike as the people you are acquainted with, and as unlike as a shepherd finds each sheep in his flock.

Small individual variations may not be readily apparent to most of us, but we sometimes find certain differences emphasized when we compare the populations of one district with those of another. Some time ago I happened to be in Scotland with a Continental ornithologist and we were both surprised to find that he did not easily recognize the notes of the chaffinch; they were not like those of the birds he knew at home (he said that they had a strong Scots accent!). Not only are there voice differences but it is also possible to distinguish Scottish (and English) chaffinches from their Continental neighbors by the color of their plumages. Plumage differences in this instance are not very marked, but they are clear enough for you to be able to distinguish the birds if you saw them both together.

It is only in certain circumstances that one would be likely to see these variants of the chaffinch together, because normally each belongs to a different place, Britain and the Continent. In other words, the differences are related to geography. These are called geographical variations, and, when they are distinct enough for the birds to be named as subdivisions of species, they are called geographical races or subspecies. Therefore, different races are only found together in the nonbreeding season when birds wander, migrate or irrupt from their breeding areas and get mixed up. The Continental chaffinch, for instance, often wanders into southern England in the winter months and may be found alongside the resident bird. In America a similar situation exists in the slate-colored junco and its relatives.

The redpolls provide a better example than the chaffinch, for there are races which are sufficiently unlike to have acquired separate common names. The lesser redpoll, resident in Britain and southern Europe, is a race of a species which has another race in northern Europe called the mealy redpoll. The mealy redpoll visits Britain in winter and is readily recognized by its larger size, and other distinctive features. Another example is the snow goose and blue goose which are not considered to be separate species but races of the same species.

Why is the slate-colored junco different from its close relatives, the pink-sided juncos? Why are the British and Continental chaffinches different, why is the lesser redpoll different from the mealy redpoll, and the snow goose from the blue goose, if they are the same species? The answer is not as difficult as it may seem. The simple clue is that the environments in which these birds live are not exactly the same. The races live in different kinds of country, and in order to be successful in living there, or in order to survive, they must adjust themselves to the conditions in which they live. If you were brought up in a country place and then find you must live in a city, it is obvious that you can only fit in if you adjust yourself to the way of life; or if born in the U.S. and went to settle in Japan, you will not be successful unless you adapt yourself to the ways of life in Japan.

Racial differences, therefore, are mainly adaptations to different environments. All sorts of factors influence changes of one kind or another. If a bird lives in a forest its plumage can be colored in many different kinds of ways, especially birds which rely on giving enemies the "slip" by playing hide-and-seek among the leaves and branches. But if such a bird tries to colonize open country, where there is little or no cover and where it cannot easily escape attack by flight, it must be colored to match the ground so that by remaining still it "melts into" its surroundings.

Camouflage, combined with temperature, seems to be responsible for an interesting variation found in species which have populations in Arctic regions. The representatives of many birds which have colonized the far north are usually whiter than their southern relatives. For example, the lesser redpoll and mealy redpoll which I mentioned earlier have a nearly white relative in the Arctic called Hornemann's redpoll: it is the "eskimo" of songbirds, for its home is the High Arctic. More striking still is the red grouse which remains unchanged all the year in Britain, but whose relative in northern Europe, the willow ptarmigan, turns white in winter. Similarly, the snow bunting and many other species get whiter, or have a white winter phase or remain white for longer periods the further north they penetrate.

The function of this variation, or the reason for this adaptation, is concerned with camouflage—obviously a white bird is less conspicuous in snow than a colored one—and also with temperature, for as you may know a white covering is a better heat insulator than a colored one.

There is another question which may have occurred to you. If the various races I have mentioned, some of which have separate names—snow goose and blue goose—look like different birds, why are they not regarded as separate species? This is more difficult to answer for it depends on what is meant by "race" and "species" and these terms are hard to define adequately. Some variations are quite clearly only very minor differences within a species, like the red on the breast of the Continental European robin, which is slightly less bright than in its British relative; while others are major differences, as between carrion crow and hooded crow. Some people argue that these two crows are not separate species but merely races of the same species. Nobody would argue about the raven being a race of either.

I will go no further in this matter of trying to define "race" and "species." I just want to show that species in obviously related groups, like raven, common crow and fish crow, are just relatives a little further removed than races which can be recognized in any one of them. In other words the evidence which can be obtained from variation in modern birds suggests that races could become species and that species, once upon a time, were races. From this it is not difficult to deduce that certain groups, like the members of the crow family, evolved from a common crow-like ancestor, a single species whose populations first showed marked individual variation, then distinct geographical races.

Here, then, we come to changes in the course of time, or evolution. The variations we find in the birds of the present day give us a pretty good idea how they evolved during their long history. Each group of similar species had a common ancestor: birds like wood thrush, Gray's thrush and the American robin; or the yellow warbler, redstart and black-poll warbler; or the black-capped chickadee, tufted titmouse, and in Britain the great tit, coal tit and marsh tit, and so on. In turn these thrush-like, warbler-like and tit-like ancestors developed from very much older types, some of which would be the common ancestors of several groups of present-day birds. The general principle is that all pigeons, for instance, evolved from one pigeon-like species far back in the history of birds.

If we follow the branches of various bird family trees back far enough where would we get to? It is known with reasonable certainty that we would get to the Jurassic Period of the Mesozoic Era, so far back in time that it is difficult for us to comprehend the distance. It is estimated that the earth was in the Jurassic stage of its existence about 167,000,000 years ago. What kind of great ancestor of all birds would we find there? Certainly none looking anything like any bird we know. It would be part bird and part reptile for it is known that birds are an offshoot of the reptiles which flourished in great numbers and diversity in the days when there were no birds or mammals, and the earth looked very different from the way it does now.

I wonder now if you have thought of an answer to the hen and egg problem. The reptilian ancestors of birds laid eggs and this of course suggests the answer that, so far as birds are concerned, the egg came first because, it can be argued, an egg laid by a reptile hatched into a bird. Probably it didn't happen just like that, but over a long period of time the reptile became less and less reptile-like and the chick more and more bird-like. Even if we are forced to pursue the answer further back, we still get an "egg" as the answer for, as you will have read on page 10, an egg is essentially a single cell and life began on the earth, long before the Jurassic Period, as a single cell.

CHAPTER XI

Instinct and Learning

YOU OFTEN HEAR people say such things as: "I instinctively put my foot down hard on the brake;" or "I instinctively shut my eyes as it flew into my face." In the first sentence the word "instinct" is used incorrectly, for a man does not drive or stop a car by instinct, even though, through experience and practice, he may come to do so without needing

Black tern and chicks.

to think about it. In the second, the word is used correctly, since every healthy man or woman shuts his or her eyes when suddenly threatened, without having learned to do so.

The term "instinctive" is used to describe behavior which does not depend on learning or previous experience, but which is typical of a species and based on biological capacity as transmitted by heredity. Instinct is defined as "a natural aptitude, an unreasonable prompting to action." (Webster.)

In birds the ability to fly, for example, is instinctive, that is, unlearned. Many people think that birds teach their young ones to fly, but this is not so. When its wings and muscles are sufficiently developed every healthy young bird can fly, even if it has been kept in a small cage to prevent it from getting any practice flights. In fact, in a natural state, the young of many birds, especially hole-nesters, such as starlings and parrots, stay in the nest until they can fly quite strongly, and then do so without any previous practice. It is true that young birds appear to increase their skill in flying after some practice, but this is probably due more to their gaining confidence than to actual learning, although it is difficult to be sure.

People often speak of "blind instinct," and it is very often true that when an animal performs an instinctive action it appears to

71

have no understanding of why it does so. In a natural state this does not matter because the instinctive behavior is nearly always "right." So when we watch birds in their natural environment they often appear to be fully aware of what they are doing and why they are doing it, when in fact they are not. That a bird acting instinctively often has little or no insight into the purpose of its behavior can often be seen when the conditions are unnatural. You will see plenty of examples if you visit a zoo in spring, since most zoos do not give all their captive birds suitable materials and conditions for nesting. As a result, when the urge to breed and nest is very strong, but the right materials and nesting places are not available, such captive birds often show nest-building behavior typical of the species, even in conditions where it is quite useless.

For example, I remember once watching in an aviary in a zoo a female olive oropendola. This is a South American bird of the icterid family, about as big as a blue jay, dark chestnut and olive green in color with bright yellow outer tail feathers and the most lovely violet-blue eyes. In a wild state the female, without any help from her mate, builds a big hanging nest of fibers, tendrils and so on, suspended from a high branch. The first stage in the building is the tying of the first fibers around the branch that is to support the nest. This captive olive oropendola had no suitable nesting material in her aviary. She had, however, somehow found a piece of thread, only an inch long. Again and again, many hundreds of times, she vainly tried to tie this scrap of thread around the branch she had chosen for the nest site. Had she had any insight into the purpose of her nest-building behavior she would have realized that the thread could not be tied around the branch no matter how many times she tried, and that it would be of no use even if it could be. She, however, just had the impulse to tie a fiber around her chosen branch, without knowing why and, as there were no long fibers available, she had selected the nearest approach to one.

Sometimes the inability of a bird to solve

Fig. 16. An artificial pond with an overhung edge presented an insoluble problem to a mother mallard and her young. The ducklings were unable to get out of the water when they needed brooding.

even the simplest problem, or what looks to us very simple, is surprising. One cold spring evening I went into a local park where there is a small ornamental pond with sides that have a concrete overhang. A mother mallard, who had been in the habit of spending much of her time in this pool, had led her newly hatched ducklings to it. Once on the water they had been unable to get off it. The three surviving ducklings, cold, soaked and miserable, cheeping plaintively, clustered below the lip of the overhang. Above them on the artificial bank squatted the worried mother mallard. She was only 5 inches away from her young ones, yet she might have been a hundred miles away for all the hope the poor ducklings had of reaching her, their sole source of warmth and hope of life. Lacking the habit of picking up her young, she had not realized (upset though she was by her ducklings' distress) that she could lift them out of the water to safety, using her bill as easily as she would pick up a frog or a crust of bread to eat.

I could give more examples, but you are sure to see many for yourself before you have watched birds very long. There is certainly a great gulf between the bird's mind and our own. But if you also begin to study human beings in an objective way, you will soon find that people, even ourselves, can often be nearly as foolish as any bird. Don't people often use their intelligence to find a good excuse for some act prompted by "blind" instinct or emotion?

Often, however, birds are able to adapt to altered circumstances. When they do this, it is difficult not to believe that they have some comprehension of the situation, however dimly grasped.

For example, both male and female pigeons incubate the eggs, the male usually sitting from about mid-morning until an hour or two before sunset, and the female the rest of the time. The bird "off duty" preens and feeds and otherwise occupies itself and quite obviously feels no urge to incubate until the normal time to relieve its mate. Now, let us suppose we drive a female pigeon off her nest and she flies into a field or on to a roof where her mate is. He seems surprised to see her. If she does not return to the nest within a few minutes, he will do so and will sit "out of turn" until the female relieves him. Evidently the sight of his mate in some way makes him realize that the eggs or young are uncovered. It is not as if the female coming off the nest were the normal procedure of nest-relief. When the cock pigeon is due to relieve his mate, she does not leave the nest until he is beside her. Once, when I was in the Army in Malta, I had a little white domestic pigeon who regarded me as her mate. When she had eggs she sat on them all the time, only coming off for food and drink. If, however, I put my hand into the nest and covered her eggs she would consider that I had taken over and would leave the nest. She would stay away quite happily until she saw me away from the nest. Then, whether she had been off for only five minutes or for five hours, she would go back at once and cover the eggs. I always thought that she gave me a very reproachful look as she did so, but that was probably imagination due to my guilty conscience!

I saw another good example of the way in which behavior typical of the species can be adapted to unusual circumstances with a pair of domestic pigeons. They had reared a young one in a nest in a shed at the end of the garden. Before it was fledged they nested again, as pigeons often do if they are well fed. This time they made a bad choice as there was a space between the nest and a wall. Now, when pigeons are building the nest the female may bring a few twigs to the site in the early stages, but the male finds and fetches most of the material and hands it over to the female who does the building. Once the eggs are laid the female does not bring nesting material, although the male may still bring more, especially in the first few days of incubation.

When this pair had been sitting on their eggs for about two weeks, their youngster of the previous brood, who had now fledged, found where his mother was sitting. He at once joined her, stood by her side, preened, fidgeted and in so doing knocked down nearly all of the precarious nest. As soon as I saw what was happening I caught him and shut him in an aviary. His mother was now sitting on the two eggs, kept in place by only one or two twigs. She made no attempt at this stage to remedy the situation. But about an hour later, at the usual time, her mate relieved her and took over the incubation of the eggs. Instead of flying off and forgetting about the nest until the evening, as she would normally have done, the female at once began to collect material and carry it to the nest site. Back and forth she flew for the next couple of hours, searching for, finding and carrying back material as diligently as any cock pigeon ever did. She did not stop until an adequate new nest had been built in place of the one her offspring had unwittingly destroyed.

What I think to be one of the most remarkable cases of learned behavior was shown by a green heron which used a piece of bread it had found, as bait. It was seen to carry the bread to the water and drop it in, then watch for and catch small fish that came to nibble at the bread. There could be no doubt that this green heron understood quite well what it was doing, for it not only retrieved the bread each time before it floated out of reach, but actually took the bread to a fresh place when it saw some fish break surface there. I have never seen anything like this. Shortly after reading about it I saw a fine heron in a park take a large piece of bread away from a duck that was pecking at it and carry it to the water. I hoped he was going to fish with it, too, but he only washed and then swallowed it!

Much of the everyday behavior of birds is a mixture of instinctive and learned behavior. A young pigeon, for example, when old enough to look after itself instinctively, pecks at any small seed-like objects it notices. But it learns, through trial and error or through the example of its parents or other adults, which particular seed-like objects are worth eating. Most young insect-eating birds instinctively seize any small living creatures they can catch. They learn, however, either from the unpleasant results of trying, or through being warned by their parents, to leave alone bad-tasting or stinging insects. When I offered the distasteful and warningly colored yellow and black cinnabar caterpillars to some red-legged partridge chicks they seized them as eagerly as they did other insects (one even did so in spite of a warning note from its bantam foster-mother), but after tasting them they rejected them and wiped their bills repeatedly on the ground to get rid of the unpleasant taste. A few days later they did not attempt to touch cinnabar caterpillars when I offered them, although they were still eager to take meal worms or grasshoppers from my hands.

Instinctive behavior may be shown toward an unnatural object as a result of learning. A budgerigar, for example, may have learned to accept its human owner in place of a mate of its own kind. It will, however, court the man or woman with just the same movements and postures as it would normally use towards another budgerigar.

SPECIES RECOGNITION

Wild birds recognize others of their species as being of the same kind as themselves. Surprisingly, however, many birds do not instinctively recognize their own species, but have to learn what they are. This they do during the time they are looked after by their parents. The learning, called "imprint-ing," takes place at a certain period of the young bird's life. For most young nestlings this seems to be shortly before leaving the nest, when they can see well and are intensely interested in all that goes on in their sight; for most active chicks it takes place in the first day or two of their lives.

Sometimes this learning is complete and irreversible. In such cases, the bird that has been "imprinted" on a wrong object in early life will never afterwards respond to its own species. I once had a magpie which had been taken as a nestling and reared by hand. When she was young her owner used to take her to work each day, put her in a cage in his busy office, and feed her every few hours. Shortly after she was able to feed herself he gave her to me. I kept her in an aviary and gave her another magpie as a companion, but she would have none of him. Later I used to let her fly free, but she never showed the slightest interest in the wild magpies that often visited the garden. She regarded human beings as her own kind and all her social responses, all her affections and her dislikes, were shown only to men and women. Such a bird as this will usually regard one particular human being as its mate in adult life. It will then often show him or her great affection, but give other people short shrift. Often a pet gray parrot that is all love and gentleness towards its master or mistress surprises visitors who try to caress or fondle it by biting them severely. The bird is not, as is often thought, being "spiteful" or "treacherous," but just responding as it would in a natural state if a strange parrot tried to come too near. Sometimes tame birds which regard humans as their kind are, all the same, a little cowed by their much larger size. Such birds usually show only affectionate and submissive behavior towards adult humans, but show the aggressive side of their social behavior toward small children. Pet birds that do this cannot safely be allowed to fly at liberty unless they are of a species too small to do much harm. If you are ever offered a tame crow or jay, for example, you would be well advised to make sure before you accept that its owner is not getting rid of it because it attacked the baby next door.

If nestlings are reared by hand from an early age, but in company with others of their own kind, they may regard both human beings *and* their own species as their own kind, or they may lose their attachment to human beings soon after they become independent. Most of the many jays I have hand-reared and kept, responded socially to me as well as to jays. These were taken from the nest when nearly ready to fly and reared with one or two other young jays. One such female jay I kept for ten years. When her first mate was accidentally killed and she was left a widow she "paired" to me, although the following year she took a mate of her own species again. In the spring, when she regarded me as her mate, she welcomed my visits to her when she was sitting, begging me for food as she sat on her eggs. But in other years I was just an interloper in her eyes, and when they were nesting she and her mate would attack me whenever I set foot in the aviary.

Sometimes birds may become "imprinted" on other species that have never acted as parents towards them. This may occur if the bird has been in the company of such species during its fledglinghood and, at the same time, has been brought up by a human or some other substitute for the natural parent. Two examples of this in my experience were another female magpie and a male wood pigeon, both of which I hand-reared when I was a boy. The magpie was reared alone and the wood pigeon with his sister. At that time I kept a lot of domestic pigeons of different breeds and colors, and these pigeons were constantly flying about the birdhouse in which the magpie and the young wood pigeon were reared. The magpie and the young cock wood pigeon (for his sister flew away and was lost) both grew up regarding domestic pigeons as their own kind. The magpie took no notice of wild magpies, not even of a fine male who courted her for several weeks at one period. The male wood pigeon, although he often flew into the surrounding woods, was not interested in other wood pigeons, but continued all his life to court and associate with domestic pigeons.

Some birds, particularly birds of social species that have a great need for companionship, will sometimes accept other creatures as social companions, even creatures as different in appearance from themselves as man, if they are isolated from their own kind. A young budgerigar that is quite normal and which recognizes its own kind can be brought to respond socially to human beings if it is isolated inside the house where it has only humans for company. Such a bird will, however, usually revert to its original condition and prefer companions of its own species if it gets the chance. It is somewhat like Robinson Crusoe who, as you will remember, had cats and goats for companions at first on his island, but did not bother much with their friendship once he had the company of Man Friday.

Birds with active chicks seem to have a considerable degree of instinctive recognition of their own species, yet at the same time the chicks can be "imprinted" on some other creature that acts as parent to them. For example, if one rears a brood of some species of pheasant, partridge or duck under a domestic hen the chicks learn to know their foster-mother very quickly. They will not leave her to follow a mother bird of their own species, even if they have the chance to do so. When they grow up, however, they usually show social responses to their own species as well as to domestic hens even though, while they were young chicks, they never saw or associated with an adult bird of their own kind.

In the case of species in which the male does not help with the young and is different from the female in appearance it is obvious that the female at least must have some unlearned ability to recognize and respond to the male. A young hen golden pheasant, for example, may not even see an adult male of her kind until she is ready to breed, yet will respond to his calls and displays. In parasitic species this causes a very interesting situation. These birds obviously cannot recognize

Fig. 17. Dunlin and golden plover show similarity in the color pattern of the breeding plumage. The golden plover's larger size and similarly marked but brighter plumage may supply a supra-normal stimulus to the dunlin in some circumstances. (See text for details)

their own species through learning. Yet, the cuckoo (like other parasitic species) recognizes its own kind; it seems likely that something occurs very similar to the "imprinting." In the cuckoo, this serves to condition the female to a particular host species. That is to say, a cuckoo who was herself reared by, say, pied wagtails will, when she is ready to breed, be attracted by nesting pied wagtails, and lay her eggs in their nests. Although this has not yet been proved to happen, we have good circumstantial evidence from the fact that different female cuckoos lay eggs resembling those of different host species.

SUPRA-NORMAL AND SUBOPTIMAL STIMULI

Earlier in this chapter I told you of the captive oropendola whose urge to build a nest was so strong that she attempted to do so with only an inch-long piece of thread. This sort of behavior is very common in birds and indeed in all other animals. If the urge to perform some activity is very strong but the "right" stimulus or "trigger" is not available, the creature concerned will often make use of some less satisfactory substitute. This is often termed responding to a "suboptimal stimulus," or in less precise but more everyday words "making do with the next best thing." Although, in the case of the poor oropendola, acting in this way achieved nothing, in a wild state the ability to respond to an inferior substitute may be useful at

times. It may, for example, mean that a bird will learn to eat a new type of food, instead of starving if bad weather or some other mishap cuts off its usual food supply.

It comes as a shock to us at first to discover that a bird may respond to an artificial object or stimulus *more* intensely than to the natural one. For example, it has been found that incubating oyster catchers and some other birds prefer a dummy egg about three times too big to one of natural size. The outsize dummy egg is not only bigger but "bigger and better" to the bird. The larger egg constitutes a "supra-normal" stimulus to the bird's incubatory and egg-retrieving habits.

These reactions to supra-normal stimuli are not at all useful but persist because birds seldom come across outsize eggs or anything of that sort.

However, it may be that some parasitic birds supply such supra-normal stimuli to their fosterers (see page 133). Possibly, also, the well-known habit of the dunlin, of flying with and following the golden plover, is based on this principle. On moors where both dunlin and golden plovers breed, pairs of each species often nest quite near to each other. When they do, you will commonly see the "off-duty" dunlin following the male golden plover, perching near it, rising at once when it takes wing and flying closely after it. The colors and markings of these two species are similar, the plover being brighter and more boldly marked as well as bigger. So this association may be due to the golden plover's supplying a supra-normal stimulus to the social instincts of the dunlin. It is possible, however, that this habit is also of some practical advantage to the dunlin, because it is a much smaller bird. Probably the nesting dunlins benefit from the wariness of the golden plover. Perhaps, also, it is able to drive off some enemies that they could not cope with.

Man has, of course, long known about the principle of supra-normal stimuli and applied them to himself. Just think of all the tasty delicacies that tempt you to eat when you are not hungry.

TAMENESS IN BIRDS

When we say that a bird is "tame" we merely mean that it has little or no fear of us. I might say, for instance, "the people next door have a tame budgerigar" or "a friend of mine has fed a robin for several months and he is now so tame that he will come into her house and take food from the table" or "the birds on many oceanic islands are quite tame." Now all these statements are true enough, but the tameness which they describe is of three different kinds.

In the first instance the tameness of the pet budgerigar is due to its having come to identify itself with human beings and to regard them as its fellows. It is a positive tameness. The bird concerned looks upon a human being as an actual or potential mate, rival or companion, as it would regard other budgerigars were it living in a natural state. Food has little or nothing to do with its feelings. Such a bird may, and sometimes does, regard the person who feeds it as a detested rival and love some other person who never feeds it.

The robin which my friend has tamed is a wild bird living a natural life in her garden. By feeding it regularly she soon taught the bird to associate her with the appearance of meal worms and other delicacies. Since the robin is not now being shot or persecuted by man, this bird was able, without misfortune to itself, gradually to overcome most of its nervousness. It still often gives its alarm call when it comes into the room and usually flies out into the garden to devour each morsel there. This kind of tameness is due to the bird's associating people, or one particular person, with food. The bird feels no affection for the person who feeds it, any more than it would feel for a seeding plant or a tree infested with edible insects.

The tameness shown by the birds of some remote islands and those of the Antarctic continent is due to the fact that there are few predators in their native haunts. Above all there are usually no predatory mammals. Compare, for example, the situation of a penguin nesting in Antarctica whose only enemies, before man and his dogs came on the scene, were the leopard seal, which was only dangerous in the water, the Antarctic skua, which killed straying or sickly young, and the scavenging sheathbill, which would take an egg whenever it got the chance—with that of a bird on the African continent with its numerous predatory birds, mammals and reptiles.

Species of birds that have lived for long periods of time where there were few or no predators have, apparently, lost their tendency to fear any strange, moving creature larger than themselves. The tameness that such birds show is due neither to learning to associate man with food nor to learning to accept him as a companion, but simply to a natural and innate lack of fear.

CHAPTER XII

Finding Food

LIKE OURSELVES, birds must eat to live. While a bird is young its parents may feed it; in some species, if it is a female, its mate may feed it during part of the breeding season. But with these exceptions each bird must catch or find every morsel it eats, and it must find enough to keep itself alive and in good health.

The food of birds falls into two main categories. First, other animals, alive or dead: from the tiny insects captured by the golden-crowned kinglet and the humming-birds to the woodchuck or rabbit taken by the golden eagle, or the dead ox or donkey eaten by the black vulture. Second, vegetable food, of which seeds and fruits are the most important, although leaves, buds, pollen and nectar are all eaten by many kinds of birds. It seems likely that the first birds to evolve were eaters of animal food, and even today insects and other small invertebrate animals, such as worms, spiders and snails, are probably birds' most important foods. There are probably many more species of birds that feed either partly or entirely on "insects" than on any other food. Also the young of many birds which, when adult, feed mostly on vegetable matter, feed or are fed at first chiefly on insects. The goldfinch, catbird and partridge are examples.

Besides their usual food many birds swallow small stones and small pieces of shell, earth or clay. In the case of seed-eating kinds the small stones or "grit" aid in the grinding up of their food in the strong, muscular gizzard. Another and usually more important reason for taking such substances is to supply the bird with lime or other minerals that may be lacking or in short supply in its usual diet. Even birds that get all their food above ground will come down for minerals. Some fruit-eating tropical pigeons, that find all their food in the tree-tops, have been seen coming to eat earth at "salt licks" on the ground and an ornithologist who was studying a colony of carmine bee-eaters in Africa found that they would eagerly come to the ground to eat crushed eggshells scattered there for them. Here we are mainly concerned with the ways by which different birds get their food. Such behavior can, however, only be understood if we also consider some other attributes of the bird, such as its beak, digestive system, size and the environment in which it lives.

INSECT-EATERS

When I use the term "insects" you must understand it as a general one for all kinds of small invertebrate animals. It would take up too much space if I were to try to talk about all the various bird species that feed largely on insects and how they go about it. So let us consider the feeding habits of a few typical birds.

The small European robin will almost certainly make its presence known by coming close, at any rate in cold weather, perching on some nearby branch or stone and watching you expectantly with its large, lustrous eye. A particular European robin may have learned to eat bread and other human food and be used to being fed by people, but any hungry robin, even if it had never seen a man before, would behave in the same way. Unlike the larger thrushes, the European robin seldom turns over dead leaves or digs to find insects. It approaches any large animals that come into its territory and watches for insects that they expose in their rooting or digging. Probably bears and wild swine were at one time the robin's chief unwitting helpers in this way, but nowadays it is more often a man digging than a pig rooting who removes the surface layer for it.

In mild weather the European robin can usually find enough to eat without the help of other animals. It hops about, watching intently and snapping up any edible small creature that it notices either on the ground or in the branches. It also catches some flying insects, although it does not do this to the same extent as many other birds. Its very large eyes enable it to see better in a dim light than most birds can. Robins continue food-seeking much later in the day and start much earlier than most other birds do. This may also have been an adaptation to enable it to take better advantage of the digging activities of wild swine and other large mammals which are usually more active at dusk and dawn than in full daylight. The European robin also eats some fruits, particularly hawthorn berries, which it swallows whole. It is unlikely that it could live for long on a vegetable diet, however useful berries may be to it as a stopgap in times of dearth.

Many other birds of the thrush family sometimes turn over the surface layer when searching for food. This behavior is particularly common in the American robin, which is the most familiar of the thrushes. You must often have seen a robin digging in a dry ditch, a pile of dead leaves, or similar place, and noted how it seizes a beakful of debris and hurls it to one side. If you have watched very closely, you may have seen that it also scratches with its feet, but this is not so effective as that of, for example, the domestic fowl. When the robin digs for hidden food it does most of the work with its bill. The robin feeds largely on earthworms and in mild, damp weather it can often find them, without the bother of digging, on lawns, football fields and similar places where man has kept the greensward unnaturally short.

The robin also feeds on fruits of almost every kind, both wild and cultivated. When it has caught a worm, you will notice that—unless the worm is very small or the bird very hungry—the robin will drag the worm around and wipe it repeatedly on the ground before eating it. This prevents its plumage from being soiled with slime, dries up what slime remains by coating it with dirt and also injures the worm so that it is less active when finally swallowed. Other thrushes feed in much the same way as the robin, although there are some minor differences. When food is hard to find in cold winters or in hot, dry summers, the English song thrush searches for snails and gets them out of their shells by hitting them on a stone, concrete path, or other hard surface, in a very special way. This breaks the apex of the shell and cracks the columella, thus rendering useless the columella muscle with which the snail retracts into its shell. Among British thrushes this behavior seems to be typical only of the song thrush, the other species not being known to crack open snails, although they sometimes swallow small ones shell and all. A blackbird has been seen to get a snail out of its shell by seizing it before it could draw right back, and then tugging and shaking it.

Starlings feed largely in open fields and other large open spaces free from cover, as well as on the same lawns and small fields as grackles and robins. You will notice, however, that they seek food in a very different way from thrushes. Instead of making short sedate little runs and hops, with long contemplative pauses, the feeding starlings bustle about at a great rate; and if a number are feeding together, those at the back of the flock continually fly forward over the others and settle in front of them. This sort of behavior is very common in species that

This pied woodpecker is feeding on a nut which it has first wedged into a small opening in the branch. This habit of using suitable holes and crevices as anvils is also common among the nuthatches. The pied woodpecker is a Eurasian species very similar in size and color to the hairy woodpecker.

habitually feed in flocks where it is a case of "first come, first served." The starling does not dig like the robin, but it searches for hidden insects by thrusting its closed bill into the grass and then opening it widely. If you hold a starling in your hand and look closely at its head, you will see that the position of the eye is such that when the bill is opened the bird can look straight down into the space cleared in this manner and immediately spot any insect or worm that has been uncovered. The starling also thrusts its closed bill into any small crevice or hole that might hide an insect and tries to enlarge it by opening its bill. It also thrusts its bill under bits of bark lying on the ground and tries to lever them over to find any insects that may be sheltering underneath. It also eats fruits and some grain and, because it often feeds in very large flocks, it sometimes does a great deal of damage to cherry orchards and on newly sown fields.

The brown creeper is one of the few birds that feeds entirely on insects and yet manages to live in the north all the year round. It finds its food on trees and in a very special-

ized and characteristic way. If you watch a brown creeper looking for food, you will see that this little brown, white-breasted bird climbs up a tree trunk (or bough) with jerky hops, probing crevices in the bark with its long, slender curved bill. When it gets near the top of the tree, or the end of the branch, it suddenly takes wing, dives down to the base of another tree and immediately begins to climb again, searching as it goes. Usually the creatures it catches are too small, or the brown creeper too far away, for us to see them. Once, however, when I had a good view of one through my binoculars, I saw quite a big spider run out of a crevice into which the bird had probed. In a flash, the brown creeper had withdrawn its bill and seized the luckless spider. Two other common species, the nuthatch and the hairy woodpecker, also feed largely on insects found on tree trunks. The nuthatch searches the bark for resting moths and other insects and only occasionally hammers or wrenches off loose bark, but the woodpecker regularly chisels away bark and dead wood and probes the holes of wood-boring insects with its long tongue. Indeed, the former gets its name from its habit of wedging beech and hazel nuts firmly into some crack in the bark so that they are held, as if in a vise, while it cracks them open with repeated hammer-like blows of its bill. The brown creeper and the woodpeckers, when on a trunk, cling with both feet and prop their stiff tail feathers against the tree to support them. The nuthatch uses only its strong feet, and so when it rests for a moment it clings with one foot and props itself with the other. Also, if the nuthatch wishes to climb down a trunk it does so head first and without any difficulty. Woodpeckers never do this but

Fig. 18. The different methods which are used to cling to a tree trunk by a nuthatch (left) and a woodpecker (right).

"go into reverse" and climb down tail first. Presumably the brown creeper may do this also, but although I have often seen brown creepers working along upside down on the underside of a branch. I have never seen one attempt to climb down a trunk either head first or tail first. Perhaps you will be lucky enough to see one do so and find out for yourself which method it uses.

Most birds, if they eat insects at all, will sometimes attempt to catch flying insects in the air. On days when all the ants are swarming (that is when the winged male and queen ants are leaving the nests on their mating flights), you may see many species of birds, from the English sparrow to the lesser black-backed gull, hawking after them. Birds which rely on catching flying insects throughout the year are usually residents in northern areas. There are the swallows (such as the barn swallow and purple martin), the swifts (for example the chimney swift), and the goatsuckers (such as the whip-poor-will and nighthawk). The flycatchers feed principally on insects caught on the wing, but also take them from the ground and from branches.

The various species of swallow and the chimney swift spend all their food-seeking time on the wing, covering quite a wide area in their search. The whip-poor-will does the same, but it feeds at or after dusk and catches moths principally. All these birds have small weak bills but very large distensible mouths and bristles jutting outward from the face that serve to entangle insects that may have been "just missed" by the snap of the bill. The flycatchers have a rather similar but longer bill. The birds perch on a convenient branch or gate, usually near, in or at the side of some little open glade or other space, such as a pond or garden among trees. When they see a flying insect they dash out in pursuit. The loud snaps of their bills can be clearly heard, and if successful they usually return to the same perch, or another one near it, to eat their prey. Although most of their food is caught in the air, the flycatchers will sometimes descend to the ground and hop about picking up insects from the short grass of a lawn or park. Many insect-eaters, such as the black-poll and other warblers, often take insects from flowers and may, either accidently or deliberately, consume some pollen or nectar when they do so. There are, however, many birds that have come to specialize in getting their food from flowers. Among the passerine birds that do this are the beautiful sunbirds of Africa and Asia, and the more somberly colored honey eaters of Australia. Besides these, there are the lories and lorikeets which are brilliantly colored honey-eating parrots of the Australasian and Pacific regions and, most famous of all, the hummingbirds of North and South America. All these have long and tubular, or brush-like, tongues for sucking up nectar or licking up nectar and pollen. None of them, however, feed only on honey (as is sometimes thought), and many visit flowers as much for the tiny insects to be found in them as for their nectar.

81

SEED-EATERS

Many small birds in different parts of the world feed largely on seeds. Most of these birds have strong, usually stout or conical, bills with which they crack the seed. They then discard the husk and swallow the kernel. This behavior is useful because there is little or no nourishment in the husk. Small birds cannot economically consume a large quantity of useless matter with their food, since they need more nourishment, compared with their bulk, to maintain body heat and supply energy. These seed-cracking small birds have been generally called "finches," and it was at one time thought that they were all closely related to each other. Studies of their behavior and anatomy have, however, now shown that this is not necessarily so. The bill structure (and related behavior) which enables them to shell seeds in this way has evolved independently in three or four different groups of small passerine birds. For example, the finches of America and Europe are not at all closely related to the so-called finches of Australia, although both groups feed largely on seeds removed from husks.

Typical American finches are the purple finch and the house finch; the latter is abundant in the Western states. Commonest of the British finches is the chaffinch. In spring and early summer pairs of chaffinches feed largely in or near their own breeding territory. At other times numbers congregate more commonly in the same area to feed. The chaffinch is mainly a ground feeder. It hops about in a shuffling way, picking up fallen seeds and insects in wooded country, gardens and even open fields. Like so many seed-eating birds it has learned to eat cultivated grains and, especially in bad weather, gathers around stockyards, poultry-runs and similar places in search of scattered wheat. It does not often take seed from growing plants or trees; indeed, I have never seen it do so, but in May and June it feeds in the trees, searching among the leaves for the caterpillars and other insects on which it then largely subsists and on which it feeds

its young. Like most insect-eating small birds and unlike most seed-eaters, the chaffinch carries food to its young in its bill and does not first swallow and then disgorge the food. The chaffinch readily learns to eat bread, cheese and other human food. It would be interesting to know whether it usually does this as a result of experimenting for itself with a strange substance or through seeing another chaffinch eating it.

The beautiful European goldfinch has a thinner and more sharply pointed bill than other finches. The goldfinch feeds particularly on the seeds of thistles, teasels and other plants with prickly heads. For removing such seeds, its bill is nicely adapted. Goldfinches are very sociable and usually keep together in family parties or small flocks, frequenting orchards, open country with some trees, and often feeding in open spaces around airports, rubbish dumps and open lands, where there are usually good crops of thistles. The goldfinch also feeds on the seeds of many other weeds, particularly dandelion, and, in winter, on the seeds of the alder tree, often in company with siskins and redpolls. Unlike the chaffinch it usually feeds above ground level. It is not unusual to see a party of goldfinches clinging to the tops of a clump of thistles as they feed on the seeds, or perched in an alder tree extracting the seeds from the alder cones. The bullfinch of Europe differs greatly from the goldfinch in appearance; it is adapted to a life in the cover of woods and copses and seldom comes far from its shelter. The bullfinch has a short curved bill very different from that of the goldfinch. This accords with the difference in their feeding habits. The bullfinch, in late winter and early spring, feeds largely on buds, and its bill is specialized for dealing with these quickly and efficiently. Its bill is also perfectly suited for collecting and cracking many kinds of seeds. Both the bullfinch and goldfinch feed much on dandelion seeds, for example, and probably the bill of the bullfinch is more efficient for cutting into the unripe heads for the green, developing seeds. But I should imagine the bullfinch would be quite unable to extract seeds from a teasel or thistle head, and I have never heard of one trying to do so. The bullfinch also feeds on the unripe seeds of willow herb. It mumbles the long pink seed pods through its bill. Presumably by use of its tongue, deftly separates out the tiny seeds and shells and swallows them, discarding the husks and vegetable down in which the growing seeds are embedded. Like the goldfinch, the bull-finch prefers to perch on plants while it feeds, and even when feeding on such low-growing species as the dandelion often alights on the stem (which bends over with its weight), in preference to standing on the ground and reaching up to the seed head. It also feeds on the seeds of such fruits as hawthorn berries and blackberries. Like other typical seed-eating birds, the bullfinch feeds its young ones largely on green, unripe seeds and carries food to them in its crop. The purple finch of the U.S. is similar to the bullfinch.

Many larger birds such as pheasants, pigeons, and some ducks eat seeds. They, however, do not shell the seed but swallow it, husk and all. The titmice and chickadees are also in part seed-eaters. They do not crack a seed as finches do but hold it beneath their feet and hammer it open with repeated pick-ax blows of their closed beaks, or by biting and worrying at it. Birds of the crow family open nuts and acorns in the same way and then devour the contents piecemeal.

BIRDS OF PREY

The birds of prey—the hawks, buzzards, eagles, falcons and their relatives, also the owls—have specialized in feeding upon animals that are large, often warm-blooded— that is to say, on other birds, mammals and reptiles. For catching, killing and eating such prey they have all developed hooked bills and strong feet with sharp curving talons. At one time it was thought that all these birds must be closely related, but we now know, from studying other aspects of their anatomy and behavior, that the owls are in no way related to the diurnal birds of prey. For similar reasons, it is now thought

that the falcons may not be related to the hawks, buzzards and eagles, but merely have come to look like hawks through evolving the same sort of "equipment" for catching and eating their prey.

Birds of prey are often disliked and shot, not only by people anxious to protect poultry or game birds but also by some silly people who think they are bad and cruel because they eat other birds. Actually, of course, they are no more cruel than the robin pulling a worm out of the lawn or a swallow catching a gnat. Some birds of prey, however, are still quite common and widely distributed in the U.S., and you should with any luck be able to watch one of them feeding without any difficulty. One is the kestrel, known in America as the sparrow hawk, a beautiful little reddish-brown falcon which you may find over almost any field or meadow where the hunter's gun does not hold sway.

When they are looking for food, the kestrels usually hover at some height above the ground. If they see nothing of interest, they fly on a little way and hover again. If, however, the movement of some suitable prey catches their eye they will drop lower, hover again, and then when they think they have a chance of seizing the mammal, suddenly dive down into the grass. If they have been lucky, they will soon rise up into view with the prey in their feet and fly off to some tree or building to eat it; if, as more often happens, the prey has escaped, they will continue hovering and searching.

The kestrel alters its hunting methods, to some extent, according to the circumstances. If it is feeding on insects, for example, it just floats gently to the ground as it knows it can catch insects with ease, but it swoops down after a mouse or bird. It will not waste energy hovering where there is a tree or telephone pole it can perch on while scanning the ground beneath. The kestrel is primarily a hunter of small mammals, particularly the field vole, but it also takes insects, lizards and such young or sickly birds as it can catch by its "hover and drop" methods. But you may sometimes see a kestrel chasing after small birds in the same dashing manner as other small falcons, such as the merlin. It would be interesting for you to try to find out whether all kestrels hunt birds in this manner or whether it is only the occasional individual that behaves in this way.

There are other birds of prey (the British sparrow hawk being the one I am most familiar with) which feed chiefly upon birds. One is most likely to see the sparrow hawk when it circles high in the air, soaring on widespread wings. This it does most often in late winter and early spring, but to some extent at other times of the year as well. When seeking food, however, the sparrow hawk does not hunt in the open sky as the bird-eating falcons do, but takes advantage of cover and relies on surprising its prey. When hunting it flies low through woods and gardens and along lanes, frequently dodging along in the shelter of a hedge or wall, rising and flying over it every hundred yards or so. In this manner it sooner or later comes suddenly on some bird and at once dashes at it. This sparrow hawk can fly very fast for a short distance. Its rounded wings and long tail give it great maneuvrability, and its long legs enable it to snatch a flying bird at almost any angle as long as it can get within reach of it. Even so, many of the birds it attacks manage to elude it and to get safely into cover before it can seize them. I once saw a sparrow hawk outwitted by its hoped-for prey in a spectacular way. The hawk, which had probably approached unseen by flying low and keeping trees and people between it and its intended victim, suddenly dashed at a house sparrow that was feeding on the ground by a pond in Kensington Gardens in London. The gulls, ducks and pigeons all swirled up into the air as the hawk came among them and the sparrow just managed in the confusion to reach a fence of stakes around some new-sown grass a few yards away. As the hawk grabbed at it the sparrow slipped through the narrow fence posts. It then crouched still on the ground only a few inches from the hawk on the other side of the fence. The hawk flew up, over the

fence and again dashed at the sparrow, which repeated its maneuver. At this point the hawk suddenly noticed the people nearby, apparently for the first time, and flew off in fright. The sparrow remained stock still on the ground by the fence for about five minutes then flew, fast and straight as an arrow, to a thick bush about 300 yards away and vanished into it. This incident illustrates an aspect of the sparrow hawk's behavior. When it has actually sighted its prey, it becomes so completely engrossed in the hunt that it often fails to notice human beings in the vicinity. Thus it has earned a reputation for fearlessness. In fact, however, it is usually very shy of man, owing to the persecution it receives from him.

The male and female sparrow hawk differ much in size, the male being only about as large as an American robin whereas the female is as big as a small domestic pigeon. This difference in size also means that they differ somewhat in their prey. The male takes mostly small birds such as sparrows, finches and warblers, but the female not only regularly takes thrushes and starlings but quite often attacks and kills birds larger than herself, such as pigeons.

We find a similar difference between the sizes (male being always much smaller) in other birds of prey that feed principally on birds, whether hawks or falcons. It is often stated that the males of all birds of prey are much smaller than the females, but this is not so. With the exception of one or two species about whose feeding habits little is known, the difference is only found in those that feed on birds, and it is only really striking in degree in those that feed chiefly on birds, such as the sparrow hawk and peregrine. No one seems to know why this should be so. It has been suggested that this difference in the size of the sexes might be useful in preventing males and females from competing too much with each other for food. I think myself it may more likely be that small birds are generally more abundant during the breeding season when the males of birds of prey have to supply all the food for their mate and family. Natural selection has possibly favored smaller size in the males of bird-eating species, since a small hawk can chase and catch a dodging small bird more successfully than a large-sized hawk can. But neither of these ideas has been proved, and if you make observations on the feeding of such birds of prey, you may be able to find out if either is correct or not.

FISH-EATERS

Most birds that eat living creatures will readily eat fish, provided these are similar in size to their usual prey. Usually, however, they can only do this as a result of the fish being stranded through some accident. There are, however, many different kinds of birds that have specialized in catching fish as their normal way of getting food. Many seize the fish with their bills. These birds have developed rather similar bills, usually long, and with some degree of serration of the edges of the mandibles to enable them to grip a slippery, struggling fish more securely. The osprey and the fish owls, as well as the U.S. national bird, the bald eagle, which seize fish with their feet, have long curving claws and rough protuberances on the soles of their toes for the same purpose.

Two "professional" fishers, the kingfishers and the herons, are fairly common and widely distributed. Although both of them are usually wary and shy of man because they are much shot at in the supposed interests of trout fishing, you should, with a little luck and a lot of patience, be able to watch both of them at work. Indeed, in places where they are not persecuted, they are quite easy to observe with the aid of binoculars.

The heron is so often seen standing stock still in shallow water that many people believe it stands and waits for fish. In fact, the heron stands this way because usually it has already seen the person watching it, is frightened of him, and consequently stops whatever it is doing, and stands ready to fly if he comes any nearer. When seeking food the heron usually wades in the shallows or, if the water is too deep, walks along the bank. It moves very slowly, and when it catches sight of a fish you can see it become tense with excitement as it halts, then, very slowly, stalks to within striking distance. Often the attempt will not succeed, and then it is rather pathetic to see the heron suddenly relax and continue its search. If it does get near enough to the fish to strike, its long neck darts out a surprising distance and with a speed that seems unbelievable after the slow preliminaries. Even so, like the human fisherman, it is often unlucky—at least those herons that I have watched have missed far more fish than they caught. The heron, although it feeds principally on fish, will readily take other animals, such as young birds and small mammals, if it gets the chance. One heron I watched would even eat bread that people were giving to ducks in the park. It would be interesting to know how it came to learn that a substance, so unlike its natural prey, was edible.

The kingfisher is most often noticed first when it is already flying away from us, low over the water, and we hear its shrill notes, or see its brilliant blue rump. It is not a difficult bird to watch, particularly if you make a point of scanning the low branches or other possible perches along the bank of likely streams or lakes *before* you are near enough to frighten the bird into taking wing. Unlike the heron, the kingfisher habitually waits and watches for its prey. It perches on a low branch and watches the water, turning its head this way and that, Suddenly, seeing a fish, it tenses itself and then dives into the water with a splash, often going right under the surface. If lucky, it rises with a fish in its bill, flies back to its perch, shifts the fish around till it is held near the tail, beats its head several times on the branch, then shifts it around again and swallows it head first.

The beating of the fish's head on the branch serves to stun it, or at least to render it less active and thus easier to swallow. It looks like an intelligent action but is, in fact, a habitual one, as was once clearly demonstrated to me. I was watching a kingfisher perched on top of a piece of iron piping which someone had stuck upright in the bed of a stream. The kingfisher dived, caught a fish, returned to its perch and at once turned and beat the fish's head in the empty air where the branch would have been, had it been perched on one. I thought it might realize its mistake and try to hit the fish on the pipe, but it was evidently satisfied by having performed its innate fish-stunning movements and proceeded to swallow its catch without bothering further.

GETTING HELP FROM OTHERS

Although, to our way of looking at things, birds are "selfish" over their food, except when they feed their mates or young, they do sometimes help others to find food, even though they do not do it intentionally. Many birds find much of their food by watching others of their species and following them. You will notice how often pigeons find food by noticing another pigeon already feeding in a tree or on the ground. It has been suggested that one of the uses of the conspicuous white or white and black color of sea birds, such as gulls, is to enable them to see others of their own kind more easily, and so gather quickly over a shoal of fish on the surface or a pailful of scraps cast from some boat into the sea.

Gulls also utter a special call when they find a large supply of food. This food call is recognized at once by other gulls, which hurry to the spot even if the calling bird is hidden from their sight by rocks or buildings. A young red-legged partridge that finds a supply of food gives calls which attract its brothers and sisters to the feast. This is very different from the behavior of a gull or young partridge that finds a single bit of food. There is no question of sharing then, and the finder tries to avoid its fellows until the food is safely swallowed.

We can see how this behavior could have evolved since it benefits the individual as well as the species. But what are the feelings of the bird which gives the food call? Is it just so excited at the sight of a lot of food that it cannot help calling out, or does it feel some of the same emotions a bird does when feeding its mate or young? The nature of the calls given, usually similar to those used when offering to feed young, suggest that the feeling may be similar too.

Many birds also make use of other animals to assist them in finding food. I have already spoken of the robin in this connection. The starling and brown-headed cowbird frequently follow grazing sheep or cattle, running about around the beasts' muzzles and catching the insects disturbed by them. The habit is still more marked in the cattle egret. This little white heron is widespread in Africa and India, has colonized parts of Central and South America, and is now invading the southern U.S. It gets most of its food by following large wild animals or domestic cattle, catching grasshoppers and other insects disturbed by their grazing and picking flies and other pests from their bodies. It would be interesting to find out whether this is an "unlearned" characteristic or whether the birds have found out by chance that there is good hunting to be had in the animals' company.

HIGHWAY ROBBERY

Many birds that normally find their own food will turn to robbery if they get the opportunity. Gulls are especially prone to rob their own fellows, and smaller species in particular suffer much from being persistently, but not always successfully, chased by gulls if the latter notice them carrying food. If one feeds the gulls in winter, one will find that the common, herring and black-backed gulls do not dare to come so close as the noisy swarm of little black-headed gulls, but hang about in the background. If one throws a piece of bread or meat too large for a black-headed gull to swallow, one will see that as soon as it gets well away with its booty it will be chased by the larger species. If a very large piece of food is given, it may change hands—or rather bills—several times before it is finally swallowed by some herring gull or greater black-back.

When seeking worms on a grass field, common and black-headed gulls walk about, peering down in front of them the same way they do when they swim looking for small creatures in shallow water. If, however, there are lapwings feeding in the same fields, the gulls usually adopt other tactics. Then, instead of bothering to search, each gull stands near one or more lapwings, often on a molehill or some other eminence that gives it a good vantage point. Every time the lapwing drags out a worm, the gull at once dashes at it with an angry scream and harries it until it drops its catch. Oddly enough the lapwing never tries to defend its food, or even to attack the gull after it has been forced to drop the worm. Paradoxically, in spring lapwings will fiercely attack gulls that come near their eggs or young and successfully drive them away.

This sort of robbery is taken a step further by the skuas. These rather hawk-like birds (in looks and behavior only, for they are in no way related to the birds of prey) are relatives of the gulls and terns and live very largely by chasing other sea birds that are carrying food and making them drop their fish. Nor do they always need to see fish in another bird's bill. They will often chase birds that show by their bulging necks and heavy flight that they have recently fed, and harry them until they disgorge their meal in fear. It is possible that the somewhat falcon-like appearance of some skuas helps them to terrify other birds. Once, when I was sitting on a cliff top in the Shetland Isles, watching the very falcon-like arctic skuas robbing puffins, I noticed how, when a skua swooped at a puffin flying home to its nest with a billful of fish, the puffin would drop all the fish and dive into the sea with an appearance of utter terror. It behaved in fact exactly as I should have expected it to do if it had actually been attacked by a falcon.

FOOD STORAGE

Most birds "live for the day" where food is concerned, whereas many mammals that eat seeds hide away quantities of them for winter food; most birds solve the problem of food shortage by migrating to areas where food can be found. There are, however, some kinds of birds that lay up stores of food for future use.

The loggerhead shrike literally "saves up for a rainy day." It feeds on large insects, lizards, fledglings of small birds, and other creatures. When hunting is good it impales its surplus catches on thorns, hence its alternative name of butcher bird. On wet mornings, when the creatures on which it feeds are less active and it has difficulty in finding food, it goes to its "larder" and uses the food hanging there for itself or its young. Most other shrikes also have this food-storing habit.

Most of the crow family also hide surplus food. Usually they bury each seed, nut or piece of bread singly in the ground or push it into a crevice in the bark of a branch or tree trunk and carefully cover it up before leaving it. If a nuthatch comes to your bird-table, you will notice, perhaps with annoyance, that it will often carry away peanut after peanut or lump after lump of bread until nothing is left.

The jay is one of the keenest food-hoarders among birds; it spends most of its time in autumn collecting and burying acorns. In years when the acorn crop is poor, oaks that have borne a plentiful supply will be visited by many jays, some of whom come from a distance to gather acorns and carry them back to their home area for storage there. Throughout the winter and early spring most jays feed largely on acorns they have hidden the previous autumn. The nutcracker, a rare relative of the jay, but common enough in parts of Europe, is even more dependent on food storing for a living. A Swedish ornithologist who has studied nutcrackers for many years found that in spring they feed not only themselves but also their young, principally on hazel nuts they have buried the previous year.

There is still a great deal to be found out about the food-storing habits of birds. It would, for example, be worth your while to try to discover whether any particular bird which you have watched hide food remembers exactly where it is hidden or whether it only finds the food again by chance through searching in likely places. The nutcracker evidently remembers exactly where it has buried food, even when snow has covered the ground meanwhile. (At any rate those Swedish nutcrackers did.) The jay often remembers exactly where it has hidden an acorn, flies straight to the spot and digs it up without any hesitation. Indeed, a jay that happens to notice some other bird near one of its hidden treasures will drive it away and then at once dig up the acorn and hide it again in a different place! On the other hand, an ornithologist who made a most careful study of the food storing of crested tits in Norway came to the conclusion that these tits rediscovered their hidden food only by searching in winter in all likely hiding places.

FUTURE SUPPLIES

It is often thought that birds must be completely harmful to those species of animals and plants they feed upon. But this is far from true. Even those birds that feed on insects or other animals usually take only the surplus of the population. Indeed, however unpleasant and (to our eyes) unfair it may be to those unfortunate individuals whom birds eat, this may often positively benefit the species by reducing the risk of disease or hunger caused through overcrowding. Birds, just like the creatures that prey on them, tend to catch most easily the injured or diseased individuals whose removal is no loss, indeed may be a considerable gain, to those that are left.

When we come to consider the relationship of birds that are partly vegetarian to the plants which they eat for food, we find many instances where both bird and plant benefit. The jay, for example, feeds largely on acorns, and much of its other food consists of caterpillars and other leaf-eating insects that infest oak trees. Of the great number of acorns that each jay buries during the

autumn many are never recovered. Perhaps the jay has mislaid them, perhaps it has no need of them all; it may be killed or die before it can dig them all up. The result is that many of these acorns are planted in places where they have a much better chance to grow than in the shade of the parent tree. Wherever jays are common you will find young oaks growing up in parks, in pine woods, and in other places where the jays have carried and buried acorns. Acorns that fall from trees can only roll downhill—if at all. But the jays carry them up hill, over rivers and lakes, and plant them far from the parent tree. Of course, the jays do not know that they are working for the future good of their species (and of man), but the effect is just the same. Other birds that bury seeds, such as tits, nuthatches and rooks, also plant many a tree that will provide food for their descendants.

Thrushes, starlings, tanagers, and many other birds help to spread the trees and plants which provide them with food. Like most other fruit-eating birds they digest only the pulp of the berries and fruits they eat. The seeds are either regurgitated through the mouth, in the same way that predatory birds disgorge pellets of fur, bones and feathers they have swallowed when feeding, or else pass right through the birds unharmed.

Seed-eating birds, such as the pheasants, finches and most pigeons, have strong muscular gizzards in which the seeds they eat are ground to pulp. Even they, however, may sometimes be instrumental in spreading their food plants. This happens if a bird dies or is killed while it still has undamaged seeds in its crop, which may then get scattered where they can grow. I remember once being surprised to see some young oat plants growing on a ledge in a sea cave in the Shetlands. When I climbed up to investigate I found they were growing out of the remains of a dead rock pigeon. After the bird had died, some of the oats it had eaten had sprouted and grown through the rotting skin and feathers.

CHAPTER XIII

Escaping from Predators

IN THE PREVIOUS CHAPTER I talked about the ways in which birds get their food. It is just as important for a bird to escape becoming the food of some other creature. In most parts of the world we no longer have to fear that a lion or some other larger animal may attack us at any moment. So we often find it difficult to realize just how important this sort of danger, and the need to be ready at any moment to try to escape from it, is in the lives of other animals. Nearly all the other things that a bird has to do can be delayed a little while, if necessary. For example, if a heron sees its foe, man, near a pond where it wants to fish, it can wait until he is gone; if a bird which is incubating becomes hungry, it can leave its eggs for a while to go to look for food. But when a peregrine falcon swoops at a pigeon, or a sparrow hawk suddenly flips over the garden wall and dashes at a sparrow feeding on the lawn, the threatened bird must immediately cease what it is doing in order to try to escape.

DANGER IN THE AIR

In most parts of the world, birds of prey are among the most serious predators on other birds. Many of them, unlike most other predators, are able to catch and kill healthy adult birds, and regularly do so. The peregrine falcon, merlin and sparrow hawk are good examples. When we speak of them as being "able to catch adult birds" we mean, of course, that they are sufficiently successful at it to be able to get their living in this way, not that each individual sparrow hawk or merlin is always successful in its pursuits. On the contrary, it will often have to make several unsuccessful attempts before it is lucky enough to be able to catch a meal for itself or its young.

All birds that are preyed on by hawks or falcons have developed patterns of behavior which aid them to escape from their predators. Birds that see a flying hawk or falcon near, either crouch motionless where they are or dart quickly into the nearest cover. Usually they utter a characteristic "hawk-alarm" note. This cry of fear may be low-pitched and soft or high and piercing, but it is always of a kind that makes it difficult to locate precisely where the sound is coming from. This call serves to warn other birds, but at the same time does not endanger the bird uttering it. The number of sounds that are difficult to pinpoint are limited so we find that the hawk-alarm calls of different birds are often much alike. That of the jay is like that of the golden pheasant, for example, although these two species are not even distantly related to each other.

Some species of birds that are gregarious and feed in flocks on the open ground or seashore, such as waders, will pack into a dense flock and then try to gain and keep a position above and just behind the bird of prey. One will often see a flock of starlings behaving in this manner with a flying sparrow hawk or kestrel. The packing into a dense flock protects the individuals, because a hawk or falcon will very seldom swoop into a dense flock of birds. It may, however, make half-hearted swoops at the flock, and if, in the resulting panic, a single bird becomes separated from the others, it will be chased immediately. But if the flocked birds can keep above and behind their enemy it is difficult for the bird of prey even to attempt this maneuver.

Ground-living birds respond differently. Birds of prey which have little chance of catching them on the wing, will search for a single bird crouching on the ground. For example, it is well known to sportsmen that red grouse will rise and fly wildly away when a golden eagle approaches, but will lie very close and be most reluctant to take wing if a peregrine falcon is in sight.

The behavior I have just spoken of serves (if successful) to prevent a bird from being seen and singled out for attack. If an attack occurs and a bird is closely pursued by a hawk or falcon, most kinds of birds try to escape either by dodging at the moment the predator tries to seize or strike them, or by trying to get into cover where the predator cannot or will not follow, or by outflying it. A jay attacked by sparrow hawks will dodge around and behind tree trunks and large branches. A woodpecker will quickly swing around so as to keep the branch to which it is clinging between itself and the enemy. Swift-flying birds—such as many doves and swallows—can outpace most hawks and many falcons, if they manage to elude the first quick dash of the hawk or the falcon's swoop. Even species that cannot do this may escape by persistent dodging. I once saw a hobby (one of Britain's smallest and swiftest falcons) trying to catch a martin right above my head. I watched for at least five minutes as the hobby dashed down at the martin, tried to seize it, missed, turned quickly and tried to seize it by flying up at it,

turned and swooped down again and so on. At almost every attack I thought the hobby had caught its prey, but each time the martin darted aside at the last moment. I thought it was bound to tire and be killed in the end but, to my surprise, it was the hobby that finally gave up. On another occasion I saw a similar performance between a merlin and a skylark, with the same sort of escape for the hunted bird.

DANGER FROM MAMMALS

Predatory mammals, such as cats and foxes, can catch healthy adult birds only if they manage to surprise them suddenly at very close quarters by stalking or ambushing them. The same is true of some snakes which often eat birds. Some mammal and reptile predators may also catch birds when they are roosting at night. Many species of owls habitually search for and catch roosting birds. Towards such enemies as these, birds behave as a rule very differently from the way they do to a flying hawk or falcon. This difference is based on the fact that such predators have no chance of catching a bird that has already seen them. When a bird sees an enemy of this category it does not flee or hide, but indulges in what is usually termed "mobbing." It approaches fairly near, sometimes very near indeed, to the predator and utters loud cries of such a kind that its whereabouts is easily located. This attracts other birds to the spot, where they join in the mobbing. They may even dart at the predator and try to strike or peck at it (nearly always from behind!) if they see a safe chance to do so. Even if they do not "pluck up courage" enough to do this, they usually show by their behavior that they would like to attack it.

You can see this mobbing behavior if you see birds following a fox on the move during the day or you disturb an owl from its roosting place in some thick holly or fir tree and it flies out and perches where other birds can see it. The loud cries and excited movements of the mobbing birds spoil the predator's chances of obtaining food, and may discourage it from hunting in that particular area again. Of course it is improbable that the birds themselves understand the "usefulness" of what they do. It is more likely that they are simply "expressing their feelings." The differences of behavior suggests that they feel only fear at the sight of a flying hawk or falcon near them, but are angry or curious as well as rather frightened by the predators which they mob. When a bird of prey is perched in full view, birds may often mob it in the same way as they do a predatory mammal. Under these circumstances, of course, it is, like the mammal, unable to take them by surprise or to swoop on them from above. Even in flight, birds of prey may be mobbed by birds of species that are too quick or too strong to be in much danger from them.

A bird suddenly surprised by a mammal usually tries to escape by flying swiftly upwards. It is not always quick enough; some bird-eating mammals have special movements for catching a rising bird. The cat, for example, stands up on its hind toes and makes a sweeping grab at the bird with its front paws, and claws stretched out and widely spread. If you have ever played with a kitten by dangling a ball of wool or a bunch of feathers on a string, you will almost certainly have seen this bird-catching movement.

Most of the creatures I have been talking about that prey on adult birds will also, naturally, catch any young or injured birds they come across, and many of them habitually seek our nests and rob them. There are some additional predators which are unable to catch healthy adult birds but take only young or wounded birds or rob nests of eggs and nestlings. Such creatures as monkeys, squirrels, rats, crows, jays, toucans and many snakes come into this category. These predators, since they are only dangerous to eggs, young and injured birds, are usually ignored except during the breeding season. But when breeding, parent birds show a violent response to these animals that threaten the safety of their young. They mob them whenever they come anywhere near their nests or young and often attack them fiercely and persistently.

DANGER FROM MAN

Man is also a predator on many kinds of birds. Most primitive peoples eat birds and their eggs and have many ingenious traps and snares with which to catch them; besides, they shoot them with arrows and blowpipe darts, rob nests and catch wild geese and ducks when they are molting and unable to fly. Generally, where this sort of primitive hunting and use of birds by man takes place, the birds behave towards man much as they do towards any other predatory mammal.

In the past few hundred years, however, man in many parts of the world has shot birds with guns. Where shooting has gone on for some time the behavior of birds is different. There is some reason to think that the very sound of a shot, in its sudden loudness, is terrifying to most birds; we have all seen domestic pigeons that have never been shot at fly up in a panic when a car backfires near them. But the most important thing about a gun is that it enables man to kill at a distance with an unseen missile. Like the swooping falcon, but to a much greater degree, he is able to span the space between himself and his victim in a minute period of time. We find that the behavior of many birds that are hunted in this manner have become adapted to this form of persecution. Birds often respond to man as they would to a flying bird of prey or may show a combination of their two main types of predator response. In parts of England where the jay is much shot at by gamekeepers and gardeners it shows an excellent example of this type of complex behavior towards man. It will flee to cover and keep a considerable distance from him, but at the same time utter the loud "mobbing" calls.

RECOGNITION OF PREDATORS

How do birds recognize predators? This is an interesting problem and not a simple one either. It can be divided into two main parts; first, is any particular predator

When trying to conceal themselves from enemies, ducks and geese crouch flat with extended necks. This behavior is not often shown as a response to humans except by young birds not yet able to fly (after they have got into cover) or by incubating females that are loath to leave their eggs. Sometimes, however, adult birds that, like this Canada goose, cannot fly because they are molting or injured, will crouch and "freeze" in this manner when a man comes in sight.

recognized instinctively or only by a process of learning; and second, in either case, what are the essential features by which the bird recognizes its enemy? There is no short and certain answer to either of these questions, as there are differences between different species of birds and between the same bird and different kinds of predators.

Most birds, in fact all species in which the matter has been investigated, appear to have an instinctive fear of flying birds of prey and to recognize them the first time they see them. The features by which an inexperienced bird recognizes a bird of prey are the short neck and blunt-looking head. Any bird that is in flight above it and has this short necked hawklike shape is feared instinctively.

In experiments it has been found that when a rough cardboard model of a flying bird cut with a short projection at one end and a long one at the other was suspended on wires and pulled blunt end first above inexperienced goslings and young willow grouse they responded to it as to a bird of prey. When, however, the same model was pulled the other way, so that it now had a long neck and appeared ducklike they were unafraid of it. Also any bird swooping down towards it signifies "hawk" to most birds. In this case,

however, the "short neck" may still be a feature, since from the angle at which it is seen the bird will appear short-necked. I have often seen feeding pigeons fly up in a panic when a new arrival swooped down to join the feast. This appears to happen when the arriving pigeon is seen suddenly quite near and at such an angle that it looks momentarily hawklike. Such mistakes appear silly to us, but no doubt they are frightening enough to the pigeons, although they soon recover when they see clearly what alarmed them. Obviously it is better to be safe than sorry. The pigeon that waited to make sure when "something hawklike" was already very close would be caught for certain if the something was a goshawk or a peregrine.

However, although birds act instinctively "on the safe side" when immediate danger from a bird of prey is concerned, they can and do learn to make distinctions in some cases. If you have kept domestic pigeons, you will know that young pigeons which have never seen a swift or a martin are frightened when they first see one high overhead, because of its hawklike shape. But they soon learn that swifts and martins are harmless. Similarly most species of birds show much more fear of those species of hawks most dangerous to them than of others that are less so. In some cases, the ability to distinguish different kinds of birds of prey may be instinctive, but it seems likely that there are also different responses which are learned.

When I was in Egypt I noticed that the pretty little brown and gray and wine-colored laughing doves—very common there in towns and gardens—showed little fear of the almost equally common black kites. Kites are largely scavengers but they do snatch up young or injured birds when they have the chance; only when a kite came

Most birds soon learn which of the mammals that they see frequently are dangerous to them and to what extent. Here herring gulls and a brown bear are looking for food on the same shore. The gull immediately in the bear's path steps hurriedly aside, lifting its wings in readiness to fly if necessary. It and its companions are, however, quite unafraid of feeding or resting near to, but out of reach of, the bear.

very close would a dove take wing. But a young laughing dove that I reared from a week old was terrified when it first saw a flying black kite and its fear took a long time to lessen even a little.

Owls seem to be instinctively recognized as enemies by many birds. However, in only a few species have experiments been made with inexperienced young birds. When I showed a live tawny owl to some tame jays that had never seen an owl before, they were very curious and somewhat alarmed, but did not get nearly so excited as wild jays usually do when they come across a similar owl by day. Even when there is an instinctive recognition of a creature as an enemy, this instinct is reinforced by learning. The young bird's first sight of an owl or cat, for example, will usually be to the accompaniment of frenzied "mobbing" from its parents.

It is not known for certain whether most birds fear man instinctively, as they fear

flying hawks, or just fear him as they usually fear at first any new, large moving object, and then later learn from experience that he is a dangerous predator. What we do know is that birds appear to recognize man largely by his upright posture. You will find that birds are usually much less afraid of you if you are lying down, or even sitting down, than if you are standing up. Once, when I was wading up to my chest in the sea, four eider ducks swam up to within a few yards to have a good look at me. It was evident that they did not recognize the queer apparition in the water as a human being. A friend of mine, who was studying little ringed plovers found, similarly, that he could get much nearer to them by crawling along the ground than by walking. The plovers even at times attacked him when he was lying down, which they never dared to do, although they obviously wanted to, when he was standing up.

Bird are always more frightened of something above them than of the same thing on a level with them. This is almost certainly because anything above it suggests to a bird the instinctively-feared flying hawk or falcon. Another attribute of man that tends to be frightening to birds is our habit of fixing both eyes on the bird and keeping them fixed on it. Now this is just what predatory birds and mammals do when they are contemplating an attack, but harmless large animals like sheep and cows, do not do.

It may well be that man is not instinctively feared as such, but that his upright posture and habit of fixing his eyes makes him, even at first sight, more alarming than other creatures of similar bulk. Of course, wherever man is in the habit of preying upon birds, they soon learn from the behavior of their parents and companions to fear him as the most dangerous enemy. There does, however, appear to be evidence suggesting that some ground-nesting birds instinctively regard man as a dangerous enemy of their eggs and young. For example, some waders put on a display to distract a hunter or dog from its young; this is so "perfect" in its likeness to an injured bird that it is difficult to think that it could have developed solely in relation to predators other than man. Most dogs will dash after any bird that flaps or flutters about on the ground. A bird does not have to give a very good appearance of real injury to fool them.

PLAYING AND "PLAYING WITH FIRE"

In our childhood we play many games— hide-and-seek for example—in which we have to escape and hide. Such games are distinctly thought out and appeal largely to our instincts. Even centuries of civilized life have not obliterated man's instinctive escaping behavior and his need to gratify it. In the life of most birds both instinct and the need to escape from enemies play a much larger part than they do in our lives. You will not be surprised that a large part of the play of birds consists of movements which, when performed in earnest, are those used to escape from predators.

You can see this particularly well with ducks when they indulge in their "water sports." Their movements consist of darting over the water surface with rapidly beating wings, suddenly diving, swimming under water and either taking wing or else at once diving again as they break surface. Both on and under the surface, and particularly at the moment of diving, the duck will suddenly change its direction. After its first excitement subsides, the playing duck slackens the rushes and dives, begins to bathe in a violent manner and the play session ends, as a rule, in a bout of bathing and preening. Now these movements of the duck at play are just like those that are used in earnest to try to escape the attacks of a sea eagle or other bird of prey. A female duck will also often use them when she is chased and worried by a drake who is not her mate. But when they perform these movements in play, ducks do not appear to be at all terrified, as they are when they perform them in earnest, but rather to be happily excited and full of the joy of life. Domestic ducks will usually play in this manner if they are let out onto their pond after having been shut up for a day or two.

It is not always easy to tell for sure if birds are playing or really frightened. For example, in many birds the tendency to escape is so strong that if young birds are reared under conditions of perfect security where they have no frequent alarms at the appearance of real predators such as they would in a natural state, their instinctive impulse to perform escaping movements becomes so strong that they will "panic" at the least thing, sometimes even at nothing at all. Since birds cannot tell us in words how they feel we have to judge from the circumstances whether this escaping behavior, when we see it for no apparent reason, is play or earnest. Once you are really familiar with any particular kind of bird, it is not so difficult to decide this as you might think. But you will find it difficult to convince anyone who does not know the species well why you drew your conclusion.

Birds often appear to enjoy themselves when they are mobbing a predator. When several jays mob a sparrow hawk, one darting in to try and strike it from behind, another dodging around a thick branch just in time as the infuriated hawk dashes at it, or when a pair of crows "dive-bomb" a buzzard, easily evading its talons as it turns over in the air to defend itself, many people think that the mobbing birds are deliberately having a game with their enemy. But I do not think this sort of behavior is ever really "play." The mobbing birds may (as in the case of crows mobbing a hawk or buzzard) know quite well how little risk they run and be correspondingly bold. They may enjoy this "playing with fire" in the same way many people enjoy sports in which they run a risk of injury or death. But they are quite "serious" about it, and the playfulness only exists in the mind of the watcher. That at least is my opinion.

Canada geese.

CHAPTER XIV

Social Life

LIKE OURSELVES, most birds are social creatures. They live in contact with others of their kind and communicate with them. Even those species which are often spoken of as "living solitary lives except in the breeding season," such as the European robin and the wheatear, are seldom really solitary. They are constantly involved with other individuals whose territories border their own. So that even they have a social life of a kind, even if—to our way of thinking—it seems a rather antisocial one. When we study birds and animals, we use the word "social" to cover all the creatures' behavior towards its own kind, including aggressive as well as friendly actions. Aggression, threat and intimidation play a large part in the lives of even the most social birds, as they do in the lives of human beings. Unlike the birds,

humans are capable of controlling their unkind impulses, but too often do not do so.

One other aspect in which the social life of birds and men agree is that, as a general rule, the worse the conditions are the more they tend to be sociable. Just as people who are lost, frightened or threatened by a common enemy tend to forget their differences, gather together and derive comfort from being together, so in cold or otherwise unfavorable weather birds tend to flock more closely than at other times. Many species that "live alone," in the sense that each lives in its own territory, gather together on migration. Many territorial birds will, in the breeding season, gather together to mob or attack any predator without regard for the territorial boundaries that are otherwise fiercely defended.

Most shorebirds are highly social and usually live in flocks except when on their breeding grounds. Often, as with these purple sandpipers in Alaska, the members of such a flock do not even maintain "individual distance" (see page 107) around themselves.

BIRD LANGUAGE

Except in fables and nursery stories birds do not and cannot talk to one another in the way we humans do. They have no language like ours, consisting of words with a particular and definite meaning. But they can and do express their feelings by uttering particular sounds, and these sounds are "understood" by other birds of the same species. Often particular movements or postures are used with particular calls, and these also are "understood" by other birds of the same species that see them.

We can, I think, get the best idea of the language of birds and how much they can communicate, if we consider how much we humans learn about each other without the need of words. Even though we have a language, we still learn a great deal about how people really feel from the tone of voice they use, from the frowns or smiles on their faces, the confident or despondent posture in which they hold themselves, and so on. Indeed, we know that people sometimes give themselves away by these things when they are trying to deceive us with words and do not want us to know how they feel.

Most birds utter many different sounds, all of which are "understood" by others of their kind and give information to them. But it is unlikely that a bird ever deliberately utters sounds in order to give information to others. It just calls out in order to relieve its feelings and, although in doing so it may give useful information to its companions, the calling bird is not aware of the fact. We can often see this clearly in relation to a bird and its enemies. If a bird calls out in alarm at the sight of man, or some other predator, others of its species are at once alerted. The usefulness of such alarm calls is obvious, and so we tend to think of the bird as deliberately warning its fellows. But if you spend much time watching birds, you will see that this is not the case. Sooner or later you will observe a bird which has seen an enemy at a good distance, and is not particularly excited or alarmed itself, slip quietly away without warning its companions. You might also see a bird that is quite alone calling in alarm just as loudly as if it had a mate or companions near that needed warning.

Often it looks as if a bird is deliberately trying to warn another, usually its mate or young. Once, when I was out in the fields, I peeped over a rough stone wall and there, only a few yards in front of me in the enclosed field, was a hen lapwing sitting on her nest. She did not notice the top of my head slowly move above the top of the wall and she sat perfectly at ease, unaware that a possible enemy was near. After a few minutes her mate came flying in. He, of course, saw me below him, swerved aside in his flight, then circled around and alighted at the far end of the field. Here he uttered his alarm call repeatedly. I do not think, however, that he was deliberately trying to inform his mate of my presence, although he may have been. It is more likely that he was just frightened and upset at seeing me so near to his mate and nest and cried out his distress without any conscious motive.

The behavior of the hen lapwing was also interesting. At her mate's first call she started out of her unconcerned mien, her feathers sleeked down in alarm as she lifted her head, and looked all around for danger, but failed to see it. She then relaxed a little, but as her mate continued to call she clearly became more and more frightened, through hearing him and "sympathizing" with his feelings. Finally, after half rising and settling back on her eggs again several times, she left the nest and flew over to her mate.

The way in which birds respond to any particular call they hear may vary greatly according to different circumstances. For example, loud singing by the males of many species tells other birds of its own kind that the singer is a male, that he is in breeding condition and in a confident frame of mind, therefore, that he is on ground to which he has laid claim, that he is on his own territory in fact. What other individuals will do when they hear his singing will depend on their circumstances. For example, an unpaired female would be attracted, would approach the singer and probably pair with him if he had no mate already. A male in the adjacent territory would sing loudly in reply, thus proclaiming *his* presence on *his* land. A male trespassing on the singer's territory would be frightened and move further away or hide himself.

You may occasionally be surprised at a bird which pays little or no attention to the alarm notes of another of its kind. The usual reason for this is that—in many birds—the same notes that are used when the bird sees danger are also used when it is frustrated, or upset for some other reason. Probably there is a difference in the tone or pitch of the call that is not noticeable to our ears, but is to those of another bird. Sometimes, however, a bird will ignore the most genuine alarm cries because it knows why they are being given and is not itself afraid. When I used to keep tame jays in aviaries, I found if I held a wild jay in my hands (as I often did because I was trying to put identification rings on all the wild jays that visited my garden) out of sight of my tame jays, its screaming would greatly alarm them and cause them to start screeching loudly also. If, however, I stood in full view of the aviary so they could see the struggling, screaming jay in my hand, they paid very little heed. This also showed the rather surprising fact that the tame jays were able to understand that a person whom they did not fear themselves could, nevertheless, be the cause of fear in other jays.

One of the most puzzling things about bird "language" is the habit some birds have of copying many sounds which they hear. Probably you have heard a jay or a starling mimicking the calls of other birds, or a tame gray parrot or budgerigar repeating words which its owner has uttered. So far as is known, this power of mimicry is found only in the great family of passerines, or song birds, and in the parrot family.

If you rear a young game bird or pigeon by itself from an early age it will, when it grows up, instinctively "speak its proper language," but some kinds of song birds will not sing their "proper songs" if they have

never heard them. They have an instinctive ability to learn the natural song at a certain time of their lives (often when they are first coming into breeding condition), but if they do not hear it sung they will learn something else, or make up a song of their own different from the normal one of their species. This ability to learn the natural song is probably linked with the ability to mimic, although the inclination to practice this ability differs greatly between species. The bullfinch is an interesting example of a bird which does not mimic other species in a wild state. But it has long been known that captive bullfinches, reared by hand from the nestling stage, could be taught to pipe tunes. The young male bullfinch learns his song from his father shortly after leaving the nest. Evidently the affection for or dependence on his father is what makes the young bullfinch learn that particular song, for he ignores other singing bullfinches but listens intently when his father sings. A young bullfinch that had been reared by canaries learned the canary's song, even though there were adult bullfinches that sang frequently in the same aviary. The young hand-reared bullfinch regards the individual who cares for it as its parent, and so is ready, if it can, to imitate the "song" it produces.

It seems very likely that the "talking" of parrots, which are not known to mimic in the wild state, comes about in much the same way. Through the parrot coming to regard people as its "friends and relations," it is attracted by the sounds they make and tries to imitate them. Since caged parrots usually crave for the company and attention of a person they are fond of, whom they have, in fact, accepted in the place of a mate of their own kind, they also profit by their mimicry, since most parrot owners will spend more time with a parrot which talks than one which does not.

However, many passerine birds indulge in vocal mimicry when they are wild and leading natural lives. Among these species are the starling, black-billed magpie and the jays. It is difficult to see any useful purpose in such mimicry. Under all the circumstances in which copied sounds are uttered one would have thought that the typical calls of the species would have been just as serviceable, indeed more so. Various suggestions have been put forward as to possible uses of mimicry, but none which, in my opinion, sound very likely. Perhaps you will, one day, solve this problem.

We can be fairly sure that birds often connect sounds with certain events. They utter a particular sound when they feel the same as they did when they first heard it. When I was studying jays I found, for example, that when alarmed or upset (because I was looking at their young), jays would often utter copied sounds as well as their own alarm note. But, *in this particular situation*, the only copied sounds they uttered were the alarm notes and calls of other birds, sounds that one would expect to have alarming associations for them. Just as tame parrots associate particular people with particular words, so I found that jays often associate a sound with the creature that makes it. I have seen both wild and captive jays (at different times) utter the "frank" call of the heron the moment they caught sight of a heron flying overhead, and my tame jays used to start barking if the spaniel from next door showed itself in my garden.

DISPLAY

The word "display" is one that you see often in bird books. It is used by ornithologists as a convenient term for any of the many different postures or movements that birds show in particular circumstances. The function of display is to elicit a particular response from some other creature, usually another bird of the same species. Sometimes a distinctive call or song may accompany the display. For example, most kinds of pigeons coo in rhythm with the movements of their bowing display when courting a female. Most displays make the bird look more conspicuous, and also make it look somewhat different from usual. When the peacock displays and spreads his glorious eye-marked train in a great shimmering halo around him, framing his blue neck and breast and crested head with his golden-green back, he looks very different from his everyday appearance with folded train.

The displays are, in fact, part of the "language" of a species and serve, like calls, to let other birds know how the displaying bird feels and what it is likely to do. It is designed to elicit a suitable response from them. Of course this response may not always be the one that the displaying bird "wants." A threat display, for example, may frighten the rival at whom it is directed and make him flee, but it may anger him and make him more likely to show fight. Clearly the displaying bird is not aware of why it displays. When it is in a certain mood it just "cannot help" posturing in a certain way.

Under many circumstances birds perform what are called "intention movements." These are movements which show that the bird is inclined to do something, such as taking wing, attacking, fleeing or building. If you have watched wild ducks, for example, you will know that, unless they are suddenly and badly frightened, they never fly without first showing signs that they are "thinking of doing so." The duck that is about to fly sleeks down its plumage, makes small upward-jerking movements of its head and crouches ready for the take-off. It may do this many times before it finally leaps into the air and flies away. If its mate is with it, you can see how infectious a bird's mood can be as, usually, the mate will soon begin to make the intention movements also and finally spring into the air at almost the same moment. We ourselves often show similar behavior. How often will a guest make the "intention movements" of rising from his chair to leave and even say, "Well, I must go now," many times before he actually gets to the point of really leaving! How often we feel sad or glad or excited in sympathy with a friend, or yawn without needing to if we see a companion yawning!

A study of intention movements gives a clue to the probable origin of the displays of birds, since we find that even elaborate displays seem to be composed mainly of

(Above) The lyrebird of Australia is famed for its magnificent tail of silvery lace-like feathers, which it uses in display. Here a male is bringing his spread tail forward over his head.

The same male in full display posture. The spread tail feathers completely cover the bird and the lyre-shaped outermost cover, from which it gets its name, are clearly visible.

intention movements. Often a display seems to consist of intention movements of two incompatible or opposite kinds of behavior. For example, the majority of threat displays show a combination of the intention movements of attacking and of the intention movements of fleeing. This is hardly surprising since birds, like ourselves, often threaten when they want to attack, but are afraid to do so.

Displays also often consist in part of what are called "displacement movements" or "displacement activities." These are actions that are irrelevant or out of context, or at least appear to us to be so. Thus, courting or threatening birds may use movements of preening or of feeding. It is generally thought that these occur when the bird is prevented from fighting or mating or whatever it "really wants" to do. In much the same way, men or women in similar situations of frustration may adjust their ties or smooth their hair unnecessarily. In many species of birds, however, certain displacement movements are shown in particular situations. For example, the peahen, when she is really stimulated by a peacock's display, pecks at the ground as if feeding in front of him, thus leading people who do not understand her behavior to think that she is looking for food and not interested in the cock. Often a displacement movement used in display differs somewhat from the same movement in its original context and serves to emphasize or exhibit some striking marking. Thus, the displacement preening of courting male ducks has come to have the special function of emphasizing the bright patches of color in their wings or, in the mandarin drake, the greatly enlarged and saillike inner secondary feather.

Courtship displays, that is, displays which take place between male and female and which serve to start or maintain an interest between them, may also appear aggressive. Some displays seem to be "built up" from the intention movements of attacking and of fleeing, but often they also involve inten-tion movements of mating as well. Whether the birds really feel frightened of their prospective mate we cannot know. Perhaps when they do, it is not quite the same sort of feeling as when they fear an enemy or a predator, but more what we should call in human relationships "shyness" or "diffidence."

Many displays that are often termed "threat displays" or "courtship displays" might better be called "self-assertive" displays since they appear just to express the general exuberance of the bird, usually a male, that is giving them. Whether the display develops into attack or sexual behavior, or just peters out, depends chiefly on the sex and behavior of the bird displayed to. In many species a male and a female bird that are paired together frequently greet each other with displays and calls that are otherwise threatening or self-assertive in character. But when they are used between mates, such displays seem to express their mutual regard for each other, rather than any hostility.

At first it may seem odd that the sort of behavior that would anger or frighten the bird if it came from a stranger or a rival, seems to be welcomed from its mate. But think for a moment and you will realize that we are like birds in this respect. We are pleased if a close friend slaps us on the back, but how annoyed we are if a casual acquaintance does so! Similarly, we hate being laughed at by anyone (because laughter is basically aggressive), but a person we like very much and trust completely can laugh at us without offending us. We do not like it if we hear other people laughing when we don't know why, but when someone we like laughs *with* us it pleases us.

Most displays are directed at the displaying bird's own species, but there is one class—distraction displays—which are directed at predators and which serve to protect the young. They are, therefore, discussed in the section on "Parents and Young" (page 121).

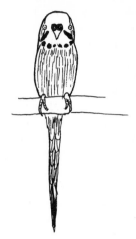

Fig. 19. The budgerigar is protectively colored; its green breast and barred blackish and yellowish upperparts make it hard to pick out when perched on a tree or feeding in the grass. But it presents to mate or rivals a bright yellow face, marked with black and mauve, in which is set the formidable bill with its blue or brown cere, and, when it flies, the brightly banded outer tail feathers catch its fellows' eyes and put them on the alert.

COLOR AND BEHAVIOR

Most bird displays involve the exhibition of colored plumage and many of their colors and markings can only be understood in reference to their social behavior. The coloration of a bird, however, can be considered from many different aspects. Here we shall consider only those aspects of a bird's color and color pattern which are closely linked with its behavior—that is to say, with the way in which its colors help it to escape from its enemies, intimidate its rivals, recognize others of its own kind and care for its young.

It is useful for a bird to be conspicuously colored for what might be termed social purposes. It will then be more easily seen and recognized by others of its own species, and it will tend to be more successful in encounters and competition with them. On the other hand the more conspicuous a bird is, the more danger it risks from enemies that hunt by sight, as do birds of prey. For avoiding such predators it is most advantageous for a bird to be colored so that it matches or blends with its surroundings and is not easily seen. Such coloring is commonly termed "cryptic," a word that means "hidden," and in this sense stands for protective coloration.

Birds which are very conspicuous, even when looked at from above (as they would be by a bird of prey), are usually large species seldom killed by hawks and falcons. The swans, the storks and the larger crows are examples. Birds which are preyed on to a large extent by other birds are usually inconspicuously colored. We find plenty of evidence suggesting that this difference has been largely brought about through natural selection operating, in this instance, through birds of prey. In species much preyed on by hawks or falcons there has been a continual weeding out of the more conspicuous individuals. Those which have had the best camouflage have been most likely to live long and reproduce others like themselves. Small birds on the whole, are preyed on by hawks and other avian enemies to a much greater extent than large ones. For this reason if we look at any group of related birds in which there is much variation in size, we find that the largest species tend to be conspicuously colored and the smallest inconspicuously colored. There are, for example, many very conspicuous large parrots and pigeons, but most of the small ones are cryptically colored. Among the Australian parrots we might compare the great white cockatoo and the great black cockatoo, both as conspicuous as their names suggest, with such small parrots as the grass parakeets, Bourke's parakeet and the budgerigar. Remember that a budgerigar of the natural wild color ("light green"), although it looks bright enough in a cage, is in fact cryptically colored and most difficult to pick out when feeding in the grass or perched among the green leaves of a tree.

The coloring of some birds, such as the mute swan, is entirely conspicuous, of others, such as the desert lark, entirely cryptic. The coloring of most birds, however, shows some degree of compromise between the need for conspicuousness for social purposes and the need for concealment from predators. This compromise may be achieved in one or more of many different ways. In many species of birds the bright markings are confined to the face, breast and underparts, while the upperparts are cryptic. The bird concerned can make itself conspicuous enough when it displays to its fellows, but when it crouches still in fear, its bright colors cannot easily be seen by an enemy overhead. You will no doubt have noticed how much easier it is to see a cock partridge if he is standing upright and unafraid, showing his gray breast with its chestnut "horseshoe" mark, than when he is crouching low in alarm with only his brown back visible. Bright colors may be hidden from view except at certain times. The male red grouse, although a little darker than the female, has a cryptic plumage. When he is feeling self-assured enough to make himself conspicuous to rival males he erects a little comb of skin over each eye. These combs are a brilliant and beautiful red so that when they are fully erected the male grouse appears to be wearing a vermillion crown, and he can be picked out by this vivid red spot on the dark moorland a hundred yards or more away. But as soon as he becomes frightened the combs collapse and shrink and are no longer noticeable. Similarly, a great many birds have white or colored markings on their outer tail feathers. These are concealed from view by the dull colored central tail feathers when the bird is resting or feeding, but are exhibited when it spreads its tail to take flight or to display the bright feathers in courtship or threat.

Many birds have what is called disruptive coloring: that is, patches, bands or spots of contrasting colors that may make them conspicuous at close quarters, but which at a little distance tend to break up their outline and make them difficult to pick out from their usual backgrounds. The ringed plover with its black and white face and white collar merges into the pebbly seashore, and even the brightly colored jay is often hard to see among foliage, the white patch on its black and blue wing appearing like a shaft of sunlight among the leaves and distracting the eye. Many truly cryptic birds also have disruptive markings—such as dark stripes which serve to conceal the eye—and no hard and fast distinction can be made between the two types of coloring. In my experience, however, the fairly bright but disruptively colored birds, such as jay and ringed plover, are always much easier, or at least less difficult, to spot than such entirely cryptic species as snipe. Whether they are also more easily seen by birds of prey and other enemies is not known, but since many bright, disruptively colored birds have most of the upper parts cryptic, and there are other species in which the more vulnerable female is cryptic but the male bright and disruptive, it is likely this is the case.

Everything we know (and there is still plenty to be found out!) suggests that one important function of bird coloring is to enable members of the same species to recognize one another quickly and efficiently and to prevent attempts at interbreeding between different species. We often find that where there are several related species living in the same country, they have striking differences of plumage, bill or eye color, even if much alike otherwise. Where this is not the case and two related species that live in the same area look very much alike, they will usually be found to differ markedly in their voices. Such differences between related species are always emphasized in their territorial and courtship displays or in their territorial songs. On the other hand, where species, or races of species, have been long isolated from contact with other close relatives they tend to lose their bright "recognition marks." This is because, under these special circumstances, the possession of bright colors or conspicuous markings no longer compensates in other ways for its drawbacks where predators are concerned. Thus, on many islands, and in some isolated areas of mountain forest, we find forms that must have been derived from those living on the mainland, but which now differ from them by having duller and less conspicuous plumage.

If a bird has some striking patch of color, it nearly always has special movements which serve to exhibit this to others of its kind. This is true not only for birds, such as the robin, which have only one such area, but also for such richly and diversely ornamented birds as the male harlequin duck and the male golden pheasant. Owls and nighthawks usually have somber and cryptic coloring, although some of them show the most beautiful intricate patterns of black, buff, brown, gray and chestnut, and the barn owl and some screech owls have much bright golden-yellow or golden-chestnut about them. This is probably because owls and nighthawks are crepuscular or nocturnal and do most of their courting or threatening in dusk or darkness when bright colors cannot be seen. Many of them, however, have conspicuous white markings, like those on the wings of the male European nightjar, which show up clearly in a dim light.

It is more difficult to think of an explanation for the fact that none of the hawks, falcons or other diurnal birds of prey have colorful plumage. Many of them have bright yellow, red or violet skin on their faces or heads but, as one naturalist pointed out many years ago, their feathers have only the same colors as those found in the fur of mammals. Many birds of prey, like many mammals, are clad in rich chestnut, golden-buff or contrasting white and black, but none have any bright green, red, blue or yellow in their plumage. Perhaps if this point interests you and you study the matter, you will yourself be the person to discover why this is so.

Birds incubating eggs or caring for young are in more danger from predators than at other times, as are their unfledged nestlings or inexperienced chicks. Where both male and females are conspicuously colored we usually find that they are either large birds with relatively few enemies or else birds, such as the kingfishers, bee-eaters and parrots, that nest in holes or covered nests where the incubating bird is hidden from view. Where the male is much more con-

A male argus pheasant in courtship display. The wings are raised and spread forward in such a way that the enormous, ocellated secondary feathers form an enormous fan, and the intricately marked primaries overlap in front of the displaying male. The female argus pheasant, as can be seen, lacks these adornments.

spicuous than the female, she alone incubates and broods the young. In many such species, particularly in those like the Argus pheasant and peacock, where the male's adornments include greatly enlarged feathers which hinder or impede flight, the male does not associate at all with his mate and their offspring. Where both sexes are alike, whether they are both conspicuous or both inconspicuous, they both care for the young and often they both take turns in incubating the eggs also. There are a few exceptions to these general rules, but they hold true for the great majority of species.

Young birds that are fed by their parents usually have the insides of their mouths brightly colored. The sudden flash of red or yellow when the mouths gape open appears to have a strong effect on the parent and to stimulate it to feed the young more zealously than might otherwise be the case. The nestlings of those species which nest in holes or which build enclosed nests usually also have conspicuous pale flanges at the corners of the mouth or pale or luminous spots at the sides of the mouth or inside it. The function of these is undoubtedly to enable the parent to see where to place the food when it feeds them in the darkness of the nest. In the case of those young birds which do not gape but

which peck the food from the parent's bill, or peck at the parent's bill to urge it to disgorge food for them, we find the parent's bill is often distinctively colored. For example, many gulls have a conspicuous orange spot on the bill, near the top of the lower mandible. The newly hatched chicks peck at this bright spot of color and by so doing soon seize the food that the parent holds for them in its billtip.

The plumage of such young birds as are reared in open nests is usually highly cryptic. Anyone who has searched for a little tern or a brood of meadowlarks knows how difficult such young are to see, even when, by watching the food-carrying parent from a distance,

The same young least tern standing on a contrasting background.

one has discovered their approximate position. The little tern is, by the way, a good example of a bird that has different types of coloring at different stages of its life. Adult little terns use flight to escape from predators and they are conspicuously clad, in bluish gray, white and black, but their young, in the first plumage, are speckly brown on the upperparts, which enables them to blend perfectly with the pebbles when they crouch motionless in response to the alarm cries of their parents.

I have said much about how being conspicuous makes a bird potentially more vulnerable to birds of prey. It does not follow, however, that among any two existing species of comparable size a greater number of the more conspicuous one will fall victim to such enemies. If a wild bird is conspicuous, it means that it can afford to be so because it has other methods than avoiding being seen for escaping from its enemies. This may be by agility in flight, as in swallows and bee-eaters, or by living near holes or crevices in which to take cover as in some desert-living wheatears, and so on. Also some conspicuous birds have distasteful flesh and so are avoided by experienced predators, at least if there is a chance of catching anything better. For example, the big and brightly colored shelduck is the least wary species of wildfowl because, thanks to its bad-tasting flesh, it is ignored by the sportsmen who constantly harry smaller and more appetizing species of ducks.

WHY BIRDS FIGHT EACH OTHER

You must often have seen birds fighting: sparrows fighting at a bird feeder, starlings bickering at dusk on their roosting ledges in some towns, two male pigeons fighting on a tree, the clouts of their wings audible a hundred yards away, or a hen partridge furiously chasing another away from her mate. Such sights show us clearly that birds of the same species do not always live at peace with each other. Now it is obvious that, in one sense, birds fight for the same reason as human beings sometimes do, because

they are angry with each other. Birds do not, however, often get angry with each other without good reason. Their fighting is useful, since it enables the winner to obtain something that it must have in order to live or to breed successfully.

The examples above give most common reasons why birds fight others of their own kind. In the case of the two sparrows trying to drive each other from the bird feeder the usefulness of the fighting is evident at once, since the winner gets the food. Many birds quarrel over food supplies, particularly in times of food shortage. However, in these quarrels one bird usually gives way without a fight when the other threatens it, but if they do fight, the fighting seldom lasts very long. The weaker bird soon gives up and flees. This type of fighting is probably of use to the species as a whole, as well as to the winner itself. It ensures that, if food is scarce and there are struggles over what little food there is, the strongest individuals will get most and they will not have to expend too much of their energy fighting off weaker competitors, while the tendency of the weaker to give up easily means that they do not run much risk of being injured by the stronger bird.

In my second example the bickering of the roosting starlings has nothing to do with food, but is concerned with maintaining what ornithologists term "individual distance." Birds of many species do not like another individual to come very close to them, and if it does, they either drive it off or else move away themselves. If you look at the roosting starlings late in the evening when they have settled down, you will see that each starling has a little clear space around itself. This space may be only as far as it can peck without moving its feet, but usually it is more than that.

We do not know for certain in what way it is useful to some birds to maintain individual distance, but the most likely reason is that it gives each bird sufficient space to take wing in an emergency without being knocked or hindered by neighboring members of the flock.

Of course the bird does not understand

why it behaves in this way. So far as we can tell it just feels uneasy or angry or afraid when another bird comes very close to it. Possibly it is a similar impulse that makes most of us, when we enter a restaurant or a train, sit down at an empty table or with a vacant seat on either side of us, if it is possible to do so. Just as even the shyest of us will sit next to a close friend or wife or relative, so birds that maintain individual distance make exceptions with individuals they are fond of. For example, if you watch some pigeons coming in and settling down at their communal roost, you will notice that each bird pecks at or moves away from any other that comes very close. But in late winter and early spring you will find that the paired pigeons that have started to roost in their breeding territories, often are huddled against each other on the same ledge. This does not disprove the theory of the use of maintaining individual distance, since two pigeons sitting side by side on a ledge with no others on it have plenty of room to maneuver if they have to take flight at some alarm.

Not all species of birds maintain individual distance, however, even when they are in flocks outside the breeding season. For example, members of a flock of purple martins may roost huddled together, and many small tropical birds also roost in contact. In these species the advantages of the extra warmth so obtained evidently outweighs the dangers involved. It is, perhaps, significant that most of the birds that do this are either very small or else tropical species that live in a climate where it is much colder at night than by day.

In the third example, the fighting pigeons, we have a case of territorial fighting, fighting for the possession of territory. There have been many definitions of the word "territory" as applied to birds. The most generally accepted way is to define it simply as a defended area, a place in which the territory owner is dominant and from which it can, and does, succeed in driving away others of its species, if it wishes to do so. Such a territory may vary in size from a few square feet with some colonial species to many acres with some predatory and insectivorous birds. The territory may be held and defended only during the breeding season or throughout most of the year. A bird of a migratory species may hold territory both in its summer home and in its winter quarters.

A breeding territory is usually first acquired by a male who then, by his calls or displays, attracts a female who wishes to breed to join him. In some species, however, the pair may form first and then go and seek a suitable breeding territory together. In most cases birds seeking a breeding territory only consider areas which provide suitable sites for the nest. This you can see particularly clearly in the case of most species that nest in holes, but are unable to make suitable holes for themselves. The supply of holes is usually limited and the territory of birds that need holes but cannot make them for themselves always centers about a potential nest hole. The nearer a trespasser comes to the hole the more fiercely will it be attacked by the owner.

The way in which a territory is useful differs a great deal in different species. To give an idea, let us consider the breeding territory of the rook, the robin and the winter territory of the mourning wheatear. The first is a common British bird, the second is found in America, and to see the mourning wheatear you would have to go to North Africa or the Middle East.

The rook nests colonially in a "rookery" of anything from two or three pairs to a hundred pairs in the same group of trees. Often there are many nests almost touching each other in the same tree. Yet each pair of rooks are masters, or rather master and mistress, of their own nest and a tiny area just around it. They need to be, as you will see if you watch for any length of time. The stories one may read in old books about the honesty of the nesting rooks towards their neighbors are, I am afraid, just stories. Any building rook that notices a neighbor's nest left unguarded has no compunction about robbing it. Many rooks' nests are destroyed again and again in their early stages through the neighbors pulling them to pieces while the owners are away getting food. This they do not do, as some people believe, to "punish" the pair concerned for some "crime" against the community, but simply because they want sticks for their own nests, and it is easier to take them from another nest than to find and break off fresh ones for themselves. But in this one instance might is *not* right in the rooks' world. Although the robbers will fight each other fiercely for a choice stick or piece of lining, as they stand on the nest they are pillaging, as soon as the rightful owners return they flee helter-skelter from them.

When you think about it, is it not a remarkable and wonderful thing that a rook is frightened of the owner of a nest it is trespassing on, even though it is not at all frightened of any other rook, just as big and strong, who is also a trespasser? It is, however, absolutely essential that rooks should behave in this way if they are to breed in colonies at all. If every rook was as bold when in a neighbor's territory as it is when it is in its own, colonial nesting would be impossible. If you ever watch nesting rooks, you will see that territorial rights are occasionally challenged. Incubating female rooks and crippled individuals may be assaulted even when on their own nests. But these are the odd exceptions that prove the general rule that the rook's tiny territory is of the utmost importance to it, enabling it to breed successfully within the colony and to combat the antisocial behavior of the individual birds comprising the colony.

The robin is a solitary nester and its territory is much larger than that of the rook. Even where robins are numerous, as in some places with lots of large gardens, lawns, fruit trees and shrubbery, each pair holds a breeding territory of about half an acre or more. Unlike the rook, whose territory only provides him with a relatively safe nesting place, robins get a lot of food within the boundaries of their territory. They also get some from neutral ground and some at times from trespassing trips into neighbors'

Fig. 20. A rook in defensive threat display, facing its enemy with raised feathers and open bill. This form of threat is shown especially by sitting females defending themselves from assault or their nests from robbery.

lands when the owners are not looking. Thus, besides providing a nesting place, the robins' territory also provides food. This is probably most important when the nestlings are young and the weather is cold or wet. At such times they cannot be left unbrooded for more than a few moments. Unlike many birds the cock robin does not help to brood the young, nor to feed his mate while she is sitting, though he does feed the young. At this time, however, possession of territory usually enables the female to find food for herself quickly and near to the nest without having to compete with other robins for it. Also if the male is able to get most of his food in the territory, it will mean that he is near enough to be able to see and give warning if any predator approaches, and be on hand to help his mate attack any nest enemy that they might be able to drive away.

Another advantage of territory-owning in a species like the robin is that it serves to space out the breeding pairs. This lessens the risk (always very great) of the nest or the newly fledged young being found by some predator. Just as if you find a wild strawberry, when out in the country, you look around nearby to see if there are any more, so a predator that has caught a tasty prey searches nearby for others like it. For this reason if there are, say, twenty nests in an acre of ground, each runs more risk of being found and robbed than it would if the same twenty nests were dispersed over twenty acres.

The mourning wheatear is a handsome black and white wheatear that lives in the desert and semi-desert regions of North Africa, Egypt and the Middle East. In the summer each pair shares a large breeding territory, usually in some remote valley in the desert. In the autumn and winter each mourning wheatear is usually alone in a territory, often at the fringe of the desert, where many mourning wheatears move after the breeding season. The chief use of the mourning wheatear's winter territory seems to be to ensure its owner sufficient food by providing it with "full hunting rights" over a considerable area. That this is so is suggested by the fact that the mourning wheatear defends its winter territory not only against others of its own species but against more distant relatives, such as the hooded wheatear and the blue rock thrush, which have similar feeding habits.

Now we come to a last example of fighting, that of the hen partridge chasing another female away, not from any particular bit of land but from anywhere near a male partridge that she herself wishes to pair with. This sort of fighting, or perhaps it is better to say this reason for fighting, is very common in birds. Often it is difficult to distinguish it from fighting over breeding territory. Indeed in the fighting of many territorial birds this factor of jealousy over the mate may also be involved: a trespasser who shows interest in the territory owner's mate will usually be attacked much more fiercely than one who does not. Male pigeons are very jealous over their mates during the nesting period. A male pigeon who is outside his territory does not, however, attack another male who comes near his mate, unless it is an individual whom he knows personally and is quite certain he can easily beat in a fight. Instead he shows a pattern of behavior known to pigeon fanciers as "driving." If his mate goes near another male pigeon, he will get between them and drive her further away. You can see this behavior to a great degree, if you watch a crowd of feral pigeons being fed in a town square on some bright spring morning. Here you will see a jealous male pigeon hurrying after his mate wherever she goes and pecking angrily at her head every time she stops to pick up a crumb of bread or a grain of corn. He cannot understand that under these unnatural conditions his mate has to go close to other male pigeons in order to get her share of food. If you watch such a pair, you will see that once the female goes well away from other pigeons her mate ceases to chase and peck at her and they stroll about or stand preening or courting together in the friendliest way. But if, now, feeling sorry for the hen and wishing to feed her, you throw her some food and in doing so attract other pigeons to the spot, the male will begin to drive his mate again as soon as another cock pigeon comes close to her.

I said at the start of this chapter that birds do not often fight without good cause, in the sense that their fighting serves to secure something useful, even essential, for the winner. But there is one common exception to this rule. If a bird has been made angry by something that it cannot or dare not attack, it may relieve its feelings by turning around and attacking some weaker creature. Often when a human being is looking at a nest of young birds, the parents, distressed and angry but not daring to attack man, will peck furiously at the earth or at branches or attack any other bird that comes near. They may get so angry that they even attack each other. This is known to behavior students as "re-directed aggression." Most of us, however, are more familiar with it as "taking it out on someone else." As you know, it is a type of behavior which is, unfortunately, as common among people who ought to know better as it is among birds who cannot know when they are being foolish or unfair.

NESTING IN COLONIES

When we considered the territory of the rook we saw some of the drawbacks of nesting colonially. Yet since so many kinds of birds do nest together in company it is evident that *for those species* the advantages must outweigh the drawbacks. These draw-

Kittiwakes at a nesting cliff. The kittiwake is more truly a bird of the sea than other "seagulls" as it seldom ventures inland. It nests in colonies on suitable cliffs. Here a party is seen leaving, probably to seek food at sea, but most members of the colony are still at their nest sites on the cliff in the background.

(Below) A nesting colony of double-crested cormorants. By nesting colonially, cormorants are able to make the fullest possible use of suitably situated trees or cliff ledges. Here each possible site in the clump of dead trees supports an occupied nest.

backs are the damage that may be done by the interference of the many quarrelsome neighbors and, more particularly, the fact that each of a group of nests in one small area is much more liable to be found by a predator than each of the same number of nests scattered over a wide area. The advantages of nesting colonially are first, that it enables more birds to breed in some suitable situation and, second, that a large number of adults are more effective than two in attacking predators.

I think the first advantage is the more important. Most birds that nest in colonies live under conditions where the country that supplies them with food covers a wide area, but the type of nesting sites they favor are in short supply. Most sea birds, for example, range widely for their food but can only find the kind of places they need for nesting in limited areas. Bank swallows like sand or earth banks with vertical exposed faces into which they can tunnel, and really suitable banks are comparatively rare.

The house martin nests naturally on cliffs where it can find some eave-like overhang of rock beneath which to build its nest. Cliffs providing such sites are not at all common and so we would expect the house martin to have evolved the habit of nesting colonially. It is only relatively lately—in birds' time on earth—that man's buildings have provided an almost limitless number of nesting places for the house martin. Colonial birds now have the habit so bred into them that they usually crowd their nests close together even when there is no need to do so.

The second advantage of colonial nesting is that there are more parent birds on hand to attack a predator. If you ever watch a crow or a hawk try to fly over a tern colony when the terns have young, you will see that it usually has a hard enough time to save itself from the bills of the "dive-bombing" terns let alone do any hunting for chicks. I once saw a falcon fly over an artificial swamp on a sewage farm where a colony of black-headed gulls were breeding. The gulls attacked so fiercely that the swift, agile little falcon had some trouble before it could get

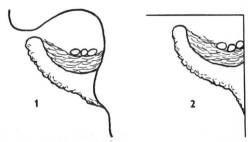

Fig. 21. Diagrammatic sketch to show, in section (1) a house martin's nest in a natural type of site under an overhanging cliff ledge, and (2) the now more usual type of site under the eaves of a house.

away safely from the danger area. However, there are some predators that the adult birds, whatever their numbers, can do nothing effective against. If, for example, a fox, a dog or a human being who wishes to take gulls' eggs or young gulls can get to the place where the nests are, the parents cannot stop it, swoop or threaten as they may.

Smaller birds that nest in colonies, such as some swallows, some weaver birds and most bee-eaters, have still greater numbers of enemies that they cannot successfully fight against, and I think that the habit of breeding in colonies has, in most cases, come about because it enabled the greatest possible number of birds to use a limited number of good nesting places.

When we see terns, or other colonial birds, attacking a hawk or other enemy that comes near their nests or young, we naturally think that the birds are deliberately banding together for mutual defense. But is this really so? I do not think it is. Rather, it appears that each bird attacks its "own" enemy without any idea that it is assisting or being assisted by its fellows when it does so. If, for example, a hawk flies over a large ternery or gullery, you will notice how it is attacked most fiercely by those whose young it is nearest. Those whose young are no longer endangered often give up the chase while the enemy is still near enough to attack other young. But, even so, the predator is attacked by many birds at once, and such attacks are much more difficult to parry or evade than the attack of a single bird or a single pair.

CHAPTER XV

Reproductive Behavior

BESIDES LOOKING after themselves, birds, like all other living creatures, must reproduce. The breeding behavior of birds appeals to us not only for scientific but for other reasons. Courting birds often utter songs that please our ears or "show off" in colorful displays that delight our eyes. Parent birds appeal to our compassion because, like ourselves, they love and cherish their young. You must not think that to have warm feelings for the birds you are studying is in any way unscientific. On the contrary, so long as you observe clearly what the bird does, you are likely to get a fuller and more complete knowledge of it if you do also appreciate it emotionally.

FINDING A MATE

Some birds, as you will have noticed, go about in pairs throughout the year. Others pair only for the breeding season or even for the rearing of a single brood. Others do not live in pairs at all but merely come together for mating. The jackdaw, the rook and the Canada goose are examples of species that usually mate for life. If one observes a flock of rooks or jackdaws at any time of year, except when the hens are busy incubating or brooding young, one will see that the pairs keep together even within the flock. A flock of rooks or jackdaws is in fact not a corporate body or society, but rather a loose association of paired birds, plus a few un-paired immatures and the odd "widow" or "widower." The individuals of the flock

may know each other (and those that nest close) very well, may even have an estab-lished hierarchy with an order of precedence, but the pair is the basic unit of their society.

Species, such as the robin, pair only for the breeding season and the male and female have no dealings, at any rate no affectionate dealings, with each other outside the breeding season. Even here, however, the same male and female may pair in successive years if they both return to the same breeding area or have lived in adjacent territories, next door to one another as it were, during the winter. In some species such as the ruff, the black grouse and some of the birds of paradise, numbers of males gather to display in the same area. Here the females visit them and mate with whichever male most takes their fancy, but there is no real pairing. The cock and hen only come together for the purpose of mating and no lasting bond is formed between them.

The ways in which those birds which form pairs find mates and "get married" varies between groups and species. Closely related species may differ in their courtship and mating behavior, and there will often be differences in the details of behavior in the pairing of individuals of the same species due to differences in the circumstances and personalities of the particular individuals. Generally, however, the male who is ready to pair makes himself conspicuous in a territory that he has acquired. He may do this by calling or singing loudly or by conspicuous displays, often by a combination of both. Soon, if he is lucky, a female who is attracted approaches him. He greets her with a display that is usually self-assertive but sometimes appeasing; he may even attack her. She responds often with an appeasing or submissive display, sometimes, however, by threatening back. But whatever happens, if she is really attracted by the male and ready to pair, she will not let herself be driven right away and she will not fight him back. Mating may take place shortly after the first encounter, or it may do so only after some days or weeks have passed and many further mutual ceremonies have been indulged in by the two birds.

With many species of birds, particularly those which nest in holes and cavities in trees or cliffs, but cannot make such holes for themselves, an important factor in pairing is the showing of a suitable hole by the male to the female. If she approves of it, she stays with him. If not, she is likely to wander away again and find a husband with a home more to her liking.

I think that it will give you a better idea of the kind of things that take place when two birds pair if I describe the pairing of two individuals of some common species. For this example I shall take the ordinary feral pigeon, so common in all our towns. This is a tame bird, easily watched, and so you will be able to see for yourself all the behavior I shall describe. Feral and domestic pigeons are the same species as their wild ancestor the rock pigeon or rock dove, and in all their displays the movements serve to show off some of the markings or colors of the wild form. In my sketches I have drawn pigeons of the natural color and pattern, which is called "blue" or "blue-barred" by pigeon fanciers. You will see many such pigeons with blue-gray heads and bodies, paler blue-gray wings crossed with two black bands and a glossy green and purple neck among the feral pigeons in any town. If you watch one of these courting or threatening, you will see how each display exhibits some striking part of its plumage. Then, if you watch, say a white domestic pigeon, you will see how it also "displays" just as if it too had an iridescent neck and conspicuous wing bars to show.

Let us then assume that we have a male feral pigeon who is ready to pair and breed, but has not yet got a mate or has been recently widowed. He has already found and claimed a nesting site, a sheltered ledge behind some ornamental stonework of an old building. From his chosen nest site, and even more often from a higher ledge of the same building, he utters his "advertising coo," a deep, moaning "Ooor, oor." This serves the same purpose as the song of many passerine birds. He frequently makes conspicuous display flights in which he claps his wings with vigorous, deep strokes and then glides with them outspread and somewhat raised, his shining neck somewhat inflated so that it bulges his chin as he flies. Whenever he alights near his home or at some feeding place where there are other pigeons, he displays self-assertively, uttering the defiant "Coo-roo-cuh-t'coo" and turning around and around with lowered head and swelling neck as he does so. Every so often, when he notices another pigeon, particularly if it is a stranger to him, he flies towards it. He claps his wings loudly, alights near or beside it and gives his bowing display. This is very similar to the self-assertive display (in fact the two intergrade), but he bows more deeply, runs up to or around the other pigeon with spread tail sweeping the ground, and when he reaches it draws himself up to his full height. As he shows off in this way he utters a version of the self-assertive "Coo-roo-cuh-t'coo" that is very deep, with the final "coo" lengthened out so that it is similar in sound to the moaning advertising coo.

If the pigeon he is displaying to is not interested in him, it will move away or ignore him, and after a little while he will lose interest in it, or he may become angry and attack it. If it is another male, it may be annoyed, and if so, the two may fight. Usually, in this situation, the fighting is half-hearted and the birds separate after a few pecks and some mutual threatening. Whenever our male bird is near his home and sees another pigeon above him in the air he gives his wing-lifting display, raising his folded wings till they are about level with his back so that the conspicuous pattern of the black bars on the pale gray is suddenly visible to the bird overhead.

One morning a female pigeon, mateless and ready to pair, arrives in his neighborhood. Perhaps she is a young bird that has never had a mate before, perhaps a recently widowed female who has wandered from her old home, as widowed female pigeons often do if no new husband is to be found there. Our male bird, as soon as he sees her approaching, flies out in a clapping and gliding display flight. This catches the eye of the female. She swerves and flies towards him as he circles back to alight near his home. The female is a little afraid, both of the male and of the strange surroundings, so she does not settle beside him, but on a higher ledge nearby. But she looks intently at the male as he turns around and around in self-assertive display, and she shows her interest clearly, for her eye sparkles as she watches him.

The male now flies over to her and displays to her. Still a little nervous of him, she moves away. But she is clearly very stimulated by the display since, even as she takes a few steps away from him, she slightly opens her wings at the shoulders and slightly spreads her tail, her rump feathers ruffle up and "a lump comes into her throat" as she slightly inflates her neck. Now the male stops his bowing display, turns a little aside from the female and begins a displacement preen behind his wing. He throws his head back and thrusts his bill between his wing and his body as if he meant to preen there. Sometimes he may actually make a preening movement when he does so. This gesture of displacement-preening behind the wing, which is performed by all species of pigeons whose behavior is known, occurs when the bird is ready or nearly ready to mate, and usually only the fact that the other partner is not yet ready prevents it from doing so. As soon as he begins to do this, the female walks up to him. He once more throws back his head and thrusts his bill between wing and

body. As he brings his head up again, he opens his bill. The female presses her body against his, reaches up and thrusts her bill into his mouth. Then, with beaks interlocked, they move their heads up and down in much the same way as a parent pigeon and a fledged young pigeon do when the former is feeding the latter. The movements are less violent, however, than in feeding young, and the male does not usually disgorge food and really feed the female, although sometimes he does. After this mutual "billing," as it is often called, the female crouches to invite the male to mate with her. Immediately after mating, the female (and often the male as well) walks a few steps in a very deliberate, proud-looking manner, with uplifted head and swelling neck, like the posture of the male in the upward movement of the bowing display. Then the pair often take wing and display-flight together, the male leading.

Shortly after this, our male pigeon flies down to the lower ledge, the female following him, and enters his nest site. Here he squats down and gives the loud, moaning advertising coo. As the female approaches, he tilts his head to eye her. He nods his head and twitches his folded wings. The female also nods as she comes near him, as she did, probably, when he displayed to her at their first meeting. This nodding of the head is derived, in an evolutionary sense, from the movement made when fixing a twig or other piece of material into the nest. It indicates that the nodding bird has found a place that it considers suitable for nesting. This seems, at least, to have been its original meaning, but, probably because the nesting bird always feels "in the right" on its nest site and ready to defend it, the nodding has also come to be used in a hostile sense. Pigeons that are fighting or threatening constantly nod "between rounds," and in this situation the nodding signifies defiance—that the nodding bird is determined to "hold its place." The one constant meaning of the nodding is that the pigeon showing it has made up its mind to stay where it is and feels that it "has a right" to do so.

As the female comes right up to the nest-

114

Fig. 22. Some stages in the pairing of two feral pigeons. (Top) The male gives his bowing display (see text for details) to female, who shows interest. (Center) The male has already once made the symbolic movement of preening behind the wing, indicating his readiness to bill and mate. The second time he does so the now eager female stretches her head towards him even before he has fully withdrawn his bill from his wing. (Bottom) The female rushes right up to the "nest-calling" male, spreading and depressing her tail as she does so (see text for full details).

calling male she is a little hesitant, particularly if she is a young female with no previous experience. She is now about to go into the very heart of the male's territory and, in spite of her eagerness, she has some fear of doing it. Indeed the male, especially if he is young and has never had a mate before, may attack her at this point. If he does so, she does not fight back but either holds her ground nodding vehemently, or flees a few steps, only to return again at once. If he continues his "nest calling," and makes no movement to attack, she finally makes a little rush, right up to him, spreading and depressing her tail as she does so, just as the male did during the bowing display, each time he rushed up to or around her. It is perhaps the passive and beseeching demeanor of the male that arouses this expression of self-assertiveness in her, since this is the only situation in which she behaves in

this way towards him. She then stands over him and preens the feathers on his head. Sometimes she may be rather aggressive and even peck his head quite roughly at first, but if so, he does not resist. He just pushes his head under her body and continues calling and twitching his wings. By hiding his head under his mate's breast he stops her from pecking him. A fighting pigeon always pecks chiefly at its enemy's head. If it cannot see the other pigeon's head, its urge to fight dies down to a great extent. Between a paired or pairing male and female, who seldom get seriously angry with each other, the hiding of the head suffices to calm the mate and stop it from attacking. After a little while the rôles may be reversed. The female then moves into the center of the nest site and calls, while the male caresses her head. Once the male and female pigeon have spent some time calling and caressing each other's head on the nest site it usually means that they have fully accepted each other and formed a pair.

In the above account, in order to be able to describe briefly all the more important items of behavior involved in the pairing of two pigeons, I have assumed the "ideal situation" of a male and a female both ready to pair when they first meet each other. It often happens like that, but at other times one or other of the birds may be more ready than its prospective partner. A male pigeon may, for example, court a female who has taken his fancy for some time before she shows interest in him, or a female "set her cap" at a particular male who attracts her for some time before he responds to her advances. Again, if our male had not owned a suitable nesting place, the two might have paired first and gone house-hunting together afterwards. In this case, the male might, just possibly, have been deserted by his bride if another male, who possessed a nest site, tried to win her from him. Or again, the pair might have met when they were too young, been attracted to one another, and kept together until they were ready to breed.

NESTING AND INCUBATION

Everyone knows that birds build nests. We all have early childhood memories of nests. I can still clearly remember how, when five years old, I found my first birds' nest, a song thrushes', and thrilled at the sight of the beautiful blue, black-spotted eggs lying against the grayish plaster lining of the nest. Many people believe that birds sleep in their nests at night, probably because they heard this in children's stories and rhymes. In fact, very few species use their nests to sleep in and, generally speaking, birds' nests can be compared with our cots and cradles, rather than with our beds or houses. They are receptacles in which the eggs can be kept safe and warm till they hatch. In many nidiculous species (the technical term for those whose young are hatched and remain

for some time as nestlings incapable of running or flying), the nest is where the young spend the first period of their lives.

These two needs, to keep the eggs or young safe and to keep them from becoming too cold, have both played an important part in the evolution of nest building. However, except in very cold climates or in species in which the parent frequently has to leave its young or eggs unattended in cool weather, safety has been of greater importance. When I use the word "safety" I mean, of course, some degree of safety and protection, since in the wild birds' life neither a bird nor its offspring is ever completely safe. This relative safety has been achieved in many different ways. The nest itself may be camouflaged so as to be difficult to see. It may be hard for predators to reach because it hangs from the tip of a slender branch such as the Baltimore oriole's or suspended over water, or among wasps' nests, as do the nests of some weavers. It may be well concealed among the ground vegetation like that of the meadowlark. In many ground-nesting birds, the nest merges into its surroundings and the plumage of the sitting bird is highly cryptic. One might find, at some time or another, the nest of a pheasant or whip-poor-will quite by accident, having failed to notice the incubating bird (whose plumage blends in so well with her surroundings) until, at the last possible moment, she might fly up to avoid being trodden on. The eggs and young of small birds are threatened by more numerous enemies than those of larger ones. Also they lose heat more quickly and die in a shorter time if left unbrooded. Hence we find that well insulated, "cosy" and well camouflaged or well hidden nests are, on the whole, commoner among small birds than among large species.

Both the male and the female robin bring sticks and other materials to their nests, but the female does most of the actual building. If you keep canaries or domestic pigeons, you know that the hen canary builds her nest without any real help from her mate. Pigeons divide the work in a different manner, the female alone building the nest but the male finding the necessary twigs or straws and carrying them to her. But all these three well-known birds, although they differ in detail, agree in that they search for suitable materials, pick them up and carry them to the place where they have chosen to nest.

Not all birds, however, build nests in this way. Owls, falcons and turkey vultures make no nest, but just scrape a slight depression on a ledge, in a hollow tree, on the ground or wherever else they decide to lay their eggs. If you have ever found the eggs of a pigeon hawk in an old crows' nest or magpies' nest, you will know that the little falcons, so far from adding any new material, actually scratch out much or all of the soft lining already there. Waterfowl (that is ducks, geese and swans), game birds and most, perhaps all, waders do not bring materials *to* the nest, but depend on what they can reach out and pull in around them as they squat in the slight hollow they have scraped at the selected place. You may have noticed when you find a mallard's nest on the ground that it consists of quite a lot of grass, dead leaves and so on, besides the down that the sitting duck has plucked from her body; but when a mallard nests in a hollow tree, where she cannot reach such material, the nest is of down only.

Even the nest of the mute swan, usually such a huge affair, has had nothing deliberately picked up and carried to it in the way that such species as the rook or the canary carry material to their nests. However, both male and female swan, when they are on the nest site and also when they are coming away from it, continually pull up vegetation and cast it down over, or alongside, their shoulders. They pick up the same pieces again and again with the result that these are dropped ever nearer to the nest site. Finally, when they are near enough to the nest site, the material is pulled in by the swan sitting there and added to the nest itself. That this behavior is instinctive and that the swans have no clear notion of what they are doing can be easily proved. If you can find a pair of swans that have decided to nest on some plot of short grass where an artificial bank rises steeply from the water's edge, you will see that their nest consists only of tufts of short grass. This is because the swans have pulled up most of their material when in the water and, because of the steep artificial bank, none of it ever fell within reach of a bird on the nest site.

I should think that quite the greatest step in the evolution of birds' nests came when the first bird to do so picked up material and actually carried it to the place where it was going to lay its eggs. Possibly this habit evolved separately in different groups of birds in response to the need for it. We find, for example, that all passerine birds, all pigeons and all hummingbirds search for nesting materials and carry them back to the nest; so do gulls, which are not at all closely related to them; the waders and auks, which are much closer relatives of the gulls, do not have this habit. Birds that had acquired this habit were no longer restricted to nesting only where there was already a suitable supporting surface for the eggs or suitable

Fig. 23. (Top) A swan's nest on a natural bank, consisting of a huge pile of water plants, and (bottom) on an artificial bank where none of the vegetable matter pulled up by the birds ever came within reach of the swan sitting on the nest.

materials within reach. They were able to build their nests in forks in trees, as do crows, magpies and many other birds, or fastened among the stems of growing reeds, like that of the long-billed marsh-wren, or suspended from the tip of a high thin branch, like that of the orioles, or plastered against the sheltering wall or roof of a cave or building, like that of the barn swallow. Although in general those birds which do not carry nesting material have been unable to use such places as the branches of trees for nesting purposes, there are one or two exceptions to this rule. Among these is the fairy tern. This is a beautiful little pure white tern that inhabits islands in the tropical oceans. It breeds in trees, but without building any nest, balancing its egg on some flat surface or slight concavity on a branch. Its chick clings tightly with its sharp claws to the branch on which it was hatched.

Of the many birds that nest in holes in trees, banks or cliffs some—for example, all the owls, falcons, ducks, pigeons and redstarts that do so—have to rely on such holes as they can find ready-made. They are quite incapable of making their own holes or even enlarging holes that are too small. Many birds do, however, make holes for themselves. You have seen the holes made by woodpeckers and have, perhaps, watched a pair at work, hammering and chiseling away the wood with their strong bills. Their tropical relatives the barbets do the same, as do many of the parrots. Bank swallows and kingfishers tunnel long holes in the earth or sand of river banks, termite nests or even the flat ground. Often there are not enough suitable holes for all the birds that want them in a district. Because of this, many hole-nesting birds in the breeding season, seek to drive away not only others of their own kind but also birds of other species that have similar nesting requirements. Nests of the hole-making species are often stolen. I expect you will have seen instances of woodpeckers being forced to desert a hole they had made because of the constant efforts of a pair of pugnacious and determined starlings.

If you are able to watch a bird building its nest closely enough to see exactly what it does, you will probably be surprised at the small number of simple movements it uses, particularly as some nests are so wonderfully strong, beautiful, and complex in construction. The material is usually fixed in place with the bill, and most birds do this in a similar way, first thrusting the material into the desired place and then making a shuddering, side-to-side movement to fix it. Much of the shaping of the nest is done with the feet, body and wings. Birds that build cup-shaped, open nests, like the crow, warbler and canary, have characteristic nest-shaping movements in which the bird lowers itself and scratches back with its feet, presses down the cup with the shoulders of its wings and the rim of the nest with its tail. Some birds, such as the orioles and troupials that build hanging nests of grasses or fibers, actually tie knots in the material.

The nests of many birds consist of two parts, an outer shell or framework of coarser, firmer or harder materials and a softer lining. For example, the goldfinch and the jay build an outer framework of twigs or sticks and then make an inner lining of thin roots and fibers, the crow lines its stick nest with hair, wool or other soft stuffs, the English sparrow's untidy-looking nest of straws and grasses is snugly lined with feathers, and so on. What tells the bird when to stop using the framework materials and to start collecting the quite different lining materials typical of its species? It seems to be the feeling of a solid support all around it that makes the bird stop using sticks or straws and start searching for fibers or feathers. This is indicated by such facts as these: when a pair of jackdaws (or crows) nest in a large cavity they bring great quantities of sticks, but if they are nesting in a very small hole, then they just line it with soft stuffs; when a jay's nest is built where it has the trunk of the tree on one side, the birds put few or no sticks on that side of the nest; similarly if a hen canary is nesting in an earthenware bowl in a cage, she uses only soft materials, such as wool and feathers, if she can get enough of them, but if she is building in a bush or tree in an outdoor aviary, she uses coarser and rougher materials for the outside part of her nest.

Sometimes we find nests that seem to us to be made of odd materials or placed in odd sites. I have seen, for instance, a feral pigeon's nest made of wire, a chaffinch's nest covered with confetti and a robin's nest in an old kettle. But if we consider such cases in detail we nearly always find that the birds behaved quite naturally but were "led astray" by the unnatural products of man introduced into their environments. Pigeons, like most other birds that build with twigs, instinctively prefer those with a somewhat tough, resilient feel about them. In other words those twigs which are "wiry" in quality. Under natural conditions, this preference for "wiriness" in the twigs is useful because such twigs will be, as a rule, more durable and easier to interlace with the others forming the nest. Now if, as sometimes happens, a cock pigeon looking for nesting material comes upon some pieces of wire that someone has thrown away, he will take them to his mate for the nest she is building. The wire is not really suitable, but the pigeon cannot know this for he judges by his instinct, and his instinctive "judgment" in this matter has evolved in relation to natural material such as stems and fallen twigs. With these, it is a case of "the wirier the better." Similarly the building hen chaffinch instinctively selects fragments with a "papery" texture, preferably light or contrasting in color, and covers the outside of her nest with them, fastening them carefully with spiderwebbing or caterpillar silk. Under natural conditions, this results in the nest being covered with lichen and matching the branches, also lichen-covered, among which it is built. Now if a chaffinch, in some lichen-less area, finds the confetti scattered near a church, it has, to her instinctive way of judging it, the same qualities as lichen and so she uses it for her nest. She does not and cannot realize that if she covers a nest, which is built on a bare bough, with brightly colored bits of confetti she may make it more conspicuous instead of camouflaging it.

The natural nesting site for the European

With the aid of a mirror this boy investigates the inside of a bumper guard on a garaged car and sees

Five young Bewick's wrens in a nest that their parents built inside the bumper guard. Such nesting places as this seem odd to us, but not to the birds that choose them. A cavity in a car is just as good as one in a tree stump.

Here one of the parent wrens waits with food for the young in its bill until the other, seen emerging, has left the nest.

119

robin is a hollow or cavity with a large opening, either in the side of a bank or on or near the ground among thick vegetation. There may be a lot of difference to us between such a place and an old kettle, lodged on its side in the hedge, but to the robin it is quite as suitable as a natural cavity. If we know the bird's instinctive behavior and take a literal "bird's eye view," we find that most odd nests and odd nesting places are not really odd after all. All the same it is worth investigating each case you come across or hear about. If you should ever find some real departure from the normal nesting behavior of the species, say a kestrel collecting nest material for itself, or a jay using wool or other soft material instead of fine roots and fibers to line its nest, that would be something really new, and it would be important to record it in an ornithological journal.

You will, perhaps, have watched a broody domestic fowl or tame canary sitting on her eggs and noticed how, when she returns to her nest, she first fluffs out the feathers on her underparts so as to expose the bare skin of her "brood patch." Then she lowers herself carefully on to the eggs and settles them comfortably into position with a side-to-side wriggling movement of her body. The majority of birds incubate their eggs in precisely the same way as do these familiar domestic ones. The emperor penguin, however, lays its egg during the Antarctic winter. On its breeding grounds no nesting materials are available and the egg would freeze if laid on the snow. But this penguin has been able to adapt itself to its environment by evolving the habit of incubating "standing up." It holds its egg on its feet, warmly tucked up into a pouch of skin of the abdomen, which folds down around it. Its relative, the king penguin, which is the large, handsome, orange-necked penguin that you can see in most zoos, hatches its egg in the same manner. The king penguin does not now breed so far south as the emperor, but there can be no doubt that it, or its forefathers, once did so. It still retains the ancestral mode of incubation instead of sitting on its egg as other species of penguins do.

A male brush turkey standing on the incubator he has made. This consists of a mound of dead leaves, twigs and earth in which the eggs are laid and buried. They are hatched by the heat generated by the decaying vegetable matter and the chicks look after themselves without help from their parents. Brush turkeys are found in Australia and belong to quite a different branch of the game bird family from the American turkey.

A different method of hatching eggs is practiced by the megapodes (mound birds) and their allies. These are a group of game birds related (but not very closely) to our familiar fowls and pheasants and are found in the East Indian and Australasian regions. All of them make use of natural or artificial "incubators" to hatch their eggs instead of sitting on them. Some of them bury their eggs in warm sand or warm volcanic earth. Others scratch up heaps of vegetation which generate heat as the contents decompose and thus supply the eggs, which the birds bury inside them, with sufficient warmth. One of the species that does this is the well known brush turkey of Australia. The male brush turkey adjusts the temperature of his mound by adding fresh material whose fermentation will increase its heat, or digging holes into the top to cool it when necessary. So efficiently does the male brush turkey control the temperature of his artificial incubator that his mate's eggs often hatch successfully even when he is in captivity in a northern zoo and has colder and more variable climate to contend with.

PARENTS AND YOUNG

After the eggs hatch, the young must be reared. Let us now consider the care of young birds, the ways in which the parents look after them or the young look after themselves. Most birds care for their young. Some insects and fishes do so too, but as a general rule the young of cold-blooded animals are left to shift for themselves from the moment they hatch. Indeed, the fact that birds, like ourselves and other mammals, "love and cherish" their offspring is one of the reasons that we feel our sympathies more easily drawn to them than to frogs or fishes, for example.

As you know, some young birds are hatched blind and helpless and remain in or very near to their nests until they can fly— for example, canaries, budgerigars and pigeons—while others run about actively and pick up food a day or two after they hatch, like chickens, ducks, geese and turkeys. The terms "nidiculous" and "altricial" are often used for inactive young birds; "nidifugous" and "precocial" for active young. In everyday speech we usually call the former "nestlings" and the latter "chicks." These are, of course, rather broad categories. There are different degrees of activity among "chicks" and different degrees of inactivity and helplessness among "nestlings." The young of some birds, such as those of gulls and nightjars, occupy an intermediate position between the active and inactive types.

Let us take a brief look at the types of young to be found in some of the main groups of birds, starting with one that has active chicks and working through to the passive nestlings. The young of the "incubator birds," the megapodes and their relatives, care for themselves from the moment they scratch free of the nest mound in which the eggs had been buried. They are hatched with the wing feathers much more developed than any other birds and are able to maintain their body temperature without parental brooding. So far as is known, they receive no help whatsoever from the adults in escaping from danger or finding food. Other young birds, even the active young waterfowl, ostriches, cassowaries, partridges and game birds, are, to a greater or lesser degree, dependent on their parents for warmth and protection, and in some cases for food as well.

The young of waterfowl, the ducks, geese and swans, are good examples of relatively independent nidifugous "chicks." Nearly all of them get their own food, unaided by the parents, although they rely on the adults for warmth and protection. Let us consider, as an example, the behavior of a typical duck, say a mother mallard with her brood. As soon as her young are dry and active the mother after first looking anxiously around to make sure that no danger threatens, leads them from the nest. She goes straight and as quickly as possible to the pond, lake or stream where she lived and fed while she was nesting. Here the ducklings find plenty of the small flies and other insects on which they chiefly feed at first. When they are tired or feel cold, the mother leads them out on to a shelving bank, an old nest or some other suitable place and broods them beneath her, dropping her wings protectively on either side to enclose them. She shelters them in this manner during rainstorms also.

If, when she is feeding or resting on the water with her ducklings scattered about chasing gnats or other prey, she sees some danger she gives low, warning calls. The ducklings at once respond by gathering together into a tight clump behind her. She then swims rapidly away, or, if a clear getaway is not possible, she crouches low among water plants or against a sheltering bank with the ducklings close beside her. Should some enemy actually discover and attack the family, then as a last resort the duck will leap forward with loud quacks of alarm; the young at once flee *away* from her, each one running, swimming or diving at full speed till it gets some distance away, and then hiding, still and silent. The mother meanwhile flaps noisily over the water, as if desperately trying to rise and fly but unable to do so. Although apparently injured she keeps just ahead of her eager pursuer at first, then she gains ground a little, then begins to rise into the air and then, having lured the foe to a safe distance she flies strongly into the air. When she feels that the coast is clear she returns to the spot where she was first frightened, or somewhere near it, and calls her ducklings out of hiding.

This "injury feigning" or "distraction display" is practiced by many different species of birds that have active chicks or that nest on or near the ground. Its purpose is to distract the predator's attention from the eggs or young and induce it to chase the parent, which it will be unable to catch. More often than not the trick is successful. I have twice seen a dog (a different one each time) jump from the bank right on to a brood of young mallard. In each case the dog ignored the ducklings and was led far from them in his eager pursuit of the loudly flapping and quacking mother duck. Although this behavior looks very intelligent, it is doubtful if the parent bird really has any understanding of what it is trying to do. The posturings vary in different species, but they are always of a kind that excite the eager pursuit of such mammal predators as foxes, dogs and men and are usually the result of the bird being "torn" between conflicting impulses. Its fear of the predator (which makes it want to flee) conflicts with its urge to attack the predator, in defense of the young, and its desire to stay with them. Still, perhaps we may at times do birds an injustice if we think that because, judged by our standards, they often seem stupid, they are always completely so. At any rate I have sometimes had the impression, when watching the distraction display of the mallard and the golden plover, that the parent bird had *some* perception of what it was doing, even though its actions were largely prompted by instinct and not by reason.

Distraction display is usually given only when an enemy whom the parent dares not attack comes close to the eggs or young. For example, our mother mallard would show fight to such enemies as a coot or a crow, which can and will kill her young, but are unlikely to be able to get the better of her should she come to grips with them.

Most other waterfowl families behave in much the same way as the mother mallard

These young Canada geese, like the young of most other waterfowl, find all their own food. They are, however, carefully watched over and protected by both parents and brooded by the mother when they need warmth or shelter from rain. This photograph shows the typical situation when a goose family is on the move, the mother goose leading, followed by the goslings, and the gander bringing up the rear.

and her young, although in swans, geese, and some others the male also helps to care for his offspring. The female red-crested pochard even helps her young to get food, diving and bringing up water weeds, which they take from her bill. So far as has been observed no other duck does this. However, little is known of the behavior of the many ducks, even those kept as ornamental birds on park lakes, because in captivity it is usual to take their eggs from them and hatch them under hens. By this means, more young can be obtained in a season, since the duck will lay several more clutches if eggs are taken as soon as laid, but less can be learned about their natural behavior. This is a thing one might watch out for if one is ever able to watch some rare or foreign duck with her young ones. For example, the rosy-billed pochard, which comes from South America, and is sometimes kept on ornamental park lakes, is a close relative of the red-crested pochard. So it is quite possible that the mother rosy-bill also gets some of her young ones' food for them, even though no one seems to have seen it happen.

The chicks of many waders, the curlew, lapwing and ringed plover, for example, also get all their own food. Their parents, like the mother mallard, only brood them at intervals, warn them of danger and endeavor to entice or drive predators away from their vicinity. The oyster catcher, however, which often nests on grassy cliff tops or other places some way from the shores where it gets most of its food, carries worms and shellfish to its young. Snipe, and probably woodcocks as well, also find food for their young. So if you ever have the chance of watching a brood of any species of wader whose parental behavior is not well known, it will be worth trying to discover whether and to what extent the parents assist their young to obtain food. For that matter, you will find it interesting enough to watch any well known species, such as the lapwing. It is always more interesting to see things for yourself than to read about them and you may, quite likely, find out some new

fact by watching even the commonest species.

Young chickens, pheasants, partridges and other game birds are less independent than ducklings or young waders. Most of them get a great deal of food for themselves, but the mother or, in species like the common partridge where both cock and hen care for the young, both mother and father, also constantly seek food for them. You have perhaps watched a farmyard hen with her brood and noticed how she calls the chicks when she has found a grub or caterpillar. They rush to her—first come first served—and snatch it up as she drops it on the ground in front of them. In some other game birds, the young always take the mother's offerings direct from her bill.

The argus pheasants and peacock pheasants have small families—only two eggs being laid in a clutch—which they must rear in jungles where there are many predatory animals and birds. Their young at first keep close behind the mother, sheltered from view by her large tail, and come forward only when she has found an insect to take it from her bill. Apart from this feeding of the young, the rôle played by the mother pheasant or the partridge pair is similar to that of the mother mallard whom we talked of earlier. This is a broad generalization.

There are, of course, small differences in behavior even between closely related species of the same family and much greater ones between members of different orders. One very important point of difference in the young of the three groups we have been considering must be mentioned. Young waterfowl grow their wing feathers last of all. Indeed, the wings themselves remain still disproportionately small when the duckling or gosling is half grown and its body covered with feathers. It is only after they are about three parts grown in size and quite independent of the mother that their wings mature, the wing feathers grow and they become able to fly. Young game birds, on the contrary, grow their wing feathers first of all (indeed they grow and molt several sets of wing feathers while they are growing to full body size), so that they can fly when they are only a week or two old, and are still little down-covered chicks. Young plovers and other waders grow all their feathers at about an even rate, just as the "nestling" type of young do, so that they can fly as soon as they are well covered in feathers, but not before.

We can easily see why it is advantageous for young game birds to be able to fly at an early age, since they are thus enabled to escape more effectively, should they be surprised by some enemy. It is, perhaps, less easy to imagine how it can be useful to water-fowl *not* to be able to fly until quite late in life or why young plovers should have the same sort of wing growth as that of nestlings. If, however, we consider the rather different problems that face such young birds when danger threatens we can find what seem to be sound reasons for their different conditions. Young game birds live on the ground and on dry land; in most cases they spend much time in the cover of long grass, shrubs or trees. They are particularly liable to attack from mammals such as cats, foxes, jackals and weasels, most of which hunt partly by scent. If, when surprised by such an enemy, the young can fly a little way off, removing themselves from the mammal's sight and breaking the scent trail, they will have a much better chance of escape than if they flee on foot. This is particularly so because game-bird families often live, or wander in search of food, among long grass or shrubs which would get in the way if the chicks should try to run off quickly in all directions. But the same plant life will, if they can fly over it, help in concealing them when they drop to the ground after a short flight, and hinder the predator from quick pursuit.

With young ducks or geese, the case is different. From many of their enemies their chances of escape are best if they stay on the water. From most predators a young duckling is more likely to escape by a quick dive, followed by an underwater swim, than it would be if it flew a short distance. With young waders, such as plovers and curlews, there has evidently been no great pressure on them, in the course of evolution, either to hasten the ability to fly, as in game birds, or to retard it until the young bird is almost fully grown and fully independent, as in water fowl. The majority of birds of this group live in open country. Their broods never number more than four. When feeding, the chicks scatter widely and, when they are being brooded by one parent, the other usually keeps a good lookout for the approach of danger. The chicks react to an alarm by crouching motionless, often first running or creeping to a depression in the soil, a clump of grass or some other place that will help to conceal them from view. Meanwhile the parents either mob or attack the intruder or endeavor to entice it away by distraction displays.

The young of birds of the rail family (crake or coot), which comprises both land-dwelling forms and semiaquatic species, are less active than young game birds or water-fowl. If one watches a brood of coots one might see that, although the chicks can run and swim at an early age, they do not venture far, but remain in their parents' nesting territory. When one of the parents finds food it does not call the chicks to it and give the morsel to the first comer, as does a parent game bird, but carries the food to one of its young and feeds it. This is not only done when they are small but, if a second brood of younger chicks is not claiming the parents' attention, they will continue to feed offspring grown almost as large as themselves. In most species of birds that have more than one brood a year the young soon part company with their parents, and if they have not done so by the time a second brood hatches, they are then driven off by their parents. Parent coots, however, remain friendly with the young of an earlier brood even after a later one has hatched. One can often see an adult pair of these birds, the nearly full-grown young of an earlier brood and chicks only a few days old peacefully associating together. Indeed with the gallinule (a rail related to the coot), the

The young of grebes can swim from an early age but for the first week or so of their lives they stay on or near the nest with one parent while the other seeks food for them. Instead of brooding their young underneath them like other birds, most grebes cradle their chicks on their backs, as this eared grebe is doing. Note how it has erected its scapular feathers to form a shelter around the chick's body. A grebe with chicks on its back can be recognized by the raised scapular feathers, which give it a "hump-backed" appearance, even at a distance or when the chicks are completely hidden from view by the sheltering plumage.

older chicks even help to feed their younger brothers and sisters.

It is probable that most other birds of the rail family behave in a similar manner. They have, however, been much less observed and most of them live among fairly dense cover of reeds and other herbage, so it is not at all easy to watch the details of their private lives. One peculiarity of this family is that their chicks are not mottled or striped (as are those of most other nidifugous birds), but are clad in sooty black down. The chicks of some of them also have brightly colored heads and bills, as in the common coot in which these parts are particularly vivid; they are bright orange-red, tinged with blue above the eyes and with brilliant red papillae around the eyes and mouth and a red, white and black beak. The function of these bright head adornments would appear to be that, like the bright mouths of nestlings that gape for food, they provide an added stimulus to the parents to feed their young. It was at one time thought that they might serve to frighten away enemies, but the fact that the frightened young coots always try to hide their brightly colored heads makes it clear that this is not so. From the point of view of safety from predators, the bright coloring is a liability rather than an asset.

The chicks of gulls and terns, although clad in down and able to run and swim at an early age, do not stray far from the nest unless they are forced to do so. Parent terns bring fish in their bills, and gulls disgorge food that they have previously swallowed, to feed their chicks. The reason why the young do not run about much is probably twofold. First, the adults of most species travel far from the nesting grounds in search of food, so it is not possible for the young to follow them on their food-seeking excursions before they can fly. Second, gulls and terns mostly nest in colonies. Birds that do this have to be content with small nesting territories. But, just as people living in a small house with a back yard may be far more angry when anyone trespasses than some great landowner, so it is that colonial species tend to be most intolerant of trespassers. Gulls and terns have no scruples about "hitting other people's children" if they catch them trespassing. A chick that strays far from home may be severely attacked, or even killed, by other adults before it can find its way back to its parents' territory. So young gulls and terns are not too venturesome and, when danger threatens, hide within their parents' territory instead of fleeing to a distance. The young of the kittiwake gull have a tendency towards a passive nestling-like condition much more than other gulls and for a good reason. Most gulls nest on the ground either in or near marshes, on cliff tops, or on broad cliff ledges. The kitti-

125

Kittiwakes build their nests of weeds and mud on small ledges of steep cliffs. Their chicks are less active then those of other gulls and always sit or stand facing inwards towards the cliff as this photograph shows. These are two patterns of behavior which lessen the risk of their falling or being blown from the nest.

wake, however, nests on small, narrow ledges on steep cliffs. Its chicks cannot leave the nest without falling to destruction. They do not try to leave, but remain sitting and standing on their small nest until they are able to fly.

People who do not understand the habits of gulls or terns can cause an immense amount of trouble and death in a colony. Even bird watchers, who should know better, are sometimes guilty of this. A party of people, for example, may visit a large and crowded colony of gulls or terns at a time when most of the young are a week or so old. As the humans approach, the adult birds fly up angry and alarmed and utter loud warning cries. Each young one runs and hides, the wiser or more experienced crouching beneath a plant or in the shelter of a stone in its parents' territory, but the more foolish or more frightened running far into neighboring territories. Some of the crouching chicks are found by the human visitors who, perhaps, cannot resist picking them up to fondle and admire them. This frightens many of the chicks so much that, on being put down, they run headlong away, forgetting all about territorial boundaries. The cries of the handled chicks further excite their already

anguished and furious parents, who swoop as near as they dare, uttering angry calls which in turn further terrify the chicks. At last the human visitors depart and the birds, the boldest first, settle again by their nests. They are still "upset," anxious and angry and, like people in a similar state, glad of any excuse to "take it out on someone." And now those chicks that have fled too far try to find their way back. Some of the more easy-going or less upset adults merely peck at the strange chicks, as they pass, but the more angry ones attack them fiercely. Some even seize a chick and carry it struggling into the air, often dropping it still further from home and among other hostile adults. Even those chicks that are "safe at home" will often take a cue from their parents and attack any intruder.

If, for any serious reason, you feel you must go into a breeding colony of gulls and terns, you can lessen the damage likely to ensue by approaching slowly so that the alarm at your presence *gradually* grows; there will then be more likelihood of chicks finding a place to crouch near home. If you must pick up a chick, grasp it gently around the wings and body, never by a leg or a wing;

A double-crested cormorant brooding its young. At this age the young are covered with short down which, together with the warmth they obtain from each others' bodies, compensates for the fact that the brooding parent can no longer completely shelter them.

Like the cormorant in the previous picture, this white-winged dove can no longer cover its well-grown young. The small, shallow nest of twigs is characteristic of the type built by most pigeons.

These young white-winged doves are nearly old enough to leave the nest and would certainly "jump overboard" if badly frightened. The bills of young pigeons appear very large in proportion to their size as can be seen by comparing those of these nestlings with that of the adult in the previous picture. This is because young pigeons have soft bills with a somewhat wider, boat-shaped lower mandible, and no feathers at the base of the bill. These are adaptations to the method of feeding in which the young bird inserts its bill into its parent's mouth, then opens it and gulps down the food which is caught in the lower mandible. As soon as the fledgling dove or pigeon reaches the age of independence, its bill hardens, the lower mandible narrows and feathers grow at the base of the bill.

it will then be less likely to struggle and call and more likely to continue crouching quietly. Put it back in its hiding place with its head as well or better hidden among the grass or between the stones as when you found it.

We now come to the many birds whose young are helpless nestlings for the first week or, more usually, two or more weeks of their lives. These include such groups of birds as the cormorants and gannets, the petrels, the birds of prey, the owls, the pigeons, the parrots, the kingfishers and all the many species in the large group of passerines or songbirds. The young of these groups differ much in their appearance when hatched—from the down-clad young owl or hawk to the naked newborn woodpecker— but all are incapable of leaving the nest either to follow the parent or to escape from enemies. Their parent must, therefore, bring all their food to them, guard them from danger and, at any rate for the first days of their lives, brood them almost constantly to keep them sufficiently warm.

Most nestlings either beg with open mouths for the parent to thrust food into their throats (as for example, young blackbirds and other passerines) or thrust their bills into their parent's throat and gulp down the food it disgorges for them (young pigeons). Young hawks and other birds of prey, and also young owls, are, however, more active at feeding time and peck the proffered morsels from the parent's bill in much the same manner as young coots do. Birds that have nestling young are also faced with another problem which does not affect those with active chicks: keeping the nest clean. In the majority of passerines, the droppings of the young while they are in the nest (but not afterwards), are enclosed in a gelatine-like capsule which enables the adult bird to carry them away without soiling itself. In some finches, such as the canary and the goldfinch, the mother eats the droppings of her young for the first few days, but as soon as the young are old enough to deposit their excrement on or over the edge of the nest, she pays no more heed to this matter. Most

pigeons and parrots and some passerines (among which are the waxbills and grass-finches from Africa and Australia which are so often kept in aviaries) make no attempt at nest sanitation. But the droppings of these birds are fairly dry and so do not soil the feathers of the young or brooding parent.

Most young birds need more easily digestible food and more animal protein than do their elders, and the behavior of the parents is adapted to these needs of the young. Many of the seed-eating finches, weavers and waxbills which when adult feed mostly on seed, feed their young at first on insects. Parent pigeons produce a curd-like substance on which their young are fed entirely for the first few days and partly thereafter.

Fig. 24. Schematic drawing of a pigeon feeding young nestlings. (Top) As seen from in front; when the young are small they often both manage to thrust their bills into the parent's mouth (from opposite sides) and are both fed at the same time. (Bottom) Side view of the same process.

An Australian boobook owl giving food to one of its three fledglings. The opaque look of the parent's eye is due to its having drawn the nictitating membrane over the eye in order to protect it from any possible accidental injury by the eager youngster.

This is formed by the degeneration and sloughing off of cells lining the crop wall, rich in nourishment and easily digested. It seems possible that similar nutritious secretions may be produced in the crop or the stomach by some of the other birds that apparently feed their young only on seeds and vegetable foods, but this is a matter that has not yet been studied in much detail. Young birds also need a lot of lime and other minerals for bone formation. For this reason young owls, during the period of maximum bone growth, digest the bones of their prey, although later in life they, like their parents, disgorge the bones undigested. If you have kept domestic pigeons, you know that when

the young are from four to twelve days' old their parents will consume large quantities of the minerals that are sold for pigeons or, if you do not give them this supplement to their grain diet, they will peck the mortar from any wall or roof where they can find it weathered and crumbling.

Nestlings have many enemies. The stage of development at which a nestling leaves the nest is, in most cases, connected with the ease with which the nest is liable to be found by a predator, and with the chances, whether good or bad, of a single fledgling being able to find a safer hiding place. Thus, we find that among hole-nesting birds, such as the starling, the young remain in the nest until

An Australian caterpillar-eater feeding its young. This photograph shows the characteristic method of parental feeding in passerines: the young bird calls for food with widely open mouth and the parent turns its head at right angles to that of the young one as it inserts the food. Notice the very small and well-camouflaged nest, now too small to contain the well-feathered young.

129

they can fly quite well. The young of birds that nest in bushes or on the ground often leave the nest before they can fly; they scatter and hide in cover for several days until they are able to fly fairly well.

The parents of most nestlings feed and watch over the safety of their young for at least for some days or often some weeks after they leave the nest. During this period the old birds also seem to get to know their young as individuals. If, while the young are in the nest, you put in among them any young of about the same age, the strangers would be fed and treated just the same as the rest by the parents, this is not the case once the young have fledged. Sometimes parent birds will adopt strange fledglings, but more often they will not. If you watch in some large garden where there are several broods of young blackbirds, for example, you will find that parents feed only their own fledglings and do not give food to the young of others, though the latter may beg to them and though they look just the same to our eyes.

Another interesting thing is that in some cases the father and mother divide the brood and, once they leave the nest, some are fed only by the mother and some only by the father. This is known to occur quite commonly in blackbirds, and I think it does in English sparrows also. At any rate when you see a fledged young sparrow following its parent about, it is always with its father *or* its mother; I have never seen both of them feeding the same young one. To prove this with any species you would have to ring the young birds with differently colored rings while still in the nest, and then make careful observations as to which parent fed each young one after they had left it.

Most birds instinctively recognize creatures that are likely to harm their young and mob or attack them on sight. The defensive attack of a parent bird is most strongly evoked if one of its young cries out in terror. Usually this cry of terror is only given when the young bird is actually seized by a predator. As soon as the parent hears this cry it is transported into a state of rage and anguish; it at once dashes to the spot and,

unless the enemy is very dangerous and terrifying, attacks it furiously. This intense emotion and its fierce expression is an unlearned response to the cry of the young and does not necessarily mean that the adult has any real grasp of the situation. A tame bird, say a tame domestic fowl, will attack you if you pick up one of her chicks and the chick screams in fear, but will take no notice if she merely sees it struggling in your hands. The sight of its struggles means absolutely nothing to her, but the moment the chick cries in terror all is changed and the placid, indifferent old broody becomes a raging fury. Similarly I once saw a young jay, that had just left the nest and was hopping about rather awkwardly on the floor of the aviary, catch its foot in some tangled grass. Feeling itself "caught" it screamed loudly in fear and at once both its parents dashed furiously down and struck it. Its cry had aroused their defensive behavior so strongly that they just had to attack *something* at the spot the cry came from. This unreflective response, which can even lead to their attacking their own young, seems stupid to us, but we can understand why such behavior has evolved. In a natural state, the terror cry of a young bird almost always means that a predator has seized it or is just about to do so. Instant attack by the parents is the only possible hope of saving the young. If they stopped to consider what was happening and what they had better do, they would do it too late.

The young bird's cry of terror has a strong effect on other young that hear it. They at once become intensely frightened and flee away from the direction of the sound. This is so with both nestlings and active chicks. Very young nestlings cannot, of course, escape, but from the time they are about half-feathered, if one of the brood gives this cry, the others jump out of the nest, and if they land uninjured, at once crawl away into the darkest place they can find and hide there. This usually means that they crawl underneath plants or among thick grass or other cover and so cannot be seen by an enemy looking down from above. This behavior gives the young their only chance of survival, since, when a predator has caught one of them, it is sure to return later for the others. However, although young that have jumped overboard in this way have some chance of surviving, they are much more likely to die of cold or to be killed by some ground-hunting predator than had they stayed in the nest during the disturbance, or at least until the proper time for them to leave. When observing nestlings you should, therefore, try to take care that they do not leave the nest too soon through your interference. Do not handle nestlings after the age at which they cower down in the nest when you approach, never shake the nest violently in climbing up to it, and do not go near if the parents are nearby, calling out in anger and alarm.

"CUCKOOS" IN THE NEST

So far we have discussed only birds that care for their own offspring. There are, however, some birds that have evolved the habit of parasitizing other species. They lay their eggs in the nests of other birds and leave them for these foster parents to look after. The best known of these is the cuckoo, the only European species to behave in this manner. However, this parasitical habit is shared by many others in the cuckoo family, by some of the cowbirds, which are members of the starling-like icterid family of the New World; by the whydahs and the cuckoo-weaver, which belong to the numerous Old World family of weaver-finches; by the honey guides, a small family of birds of dull coloring but interesting behavior found in Africa and Asia, and by the black-headed duck of South America.

The parasitic habits of the European cuckoo were well known even in antiquity, and in more recent years the work of many observers has given us a pretty complete picture of this side of its life. The female cuckoo lays her egg in the host's nest, first seizing one of its eggs (which she later carries off and eats) in her bill. The young cuckoo, while still blind and naked, gets any other young or eggs that are in the nest one by one onto its hollow back, climbs backward up the side of the nest with them and heaves them overboard. The European cuckoo usually lays in the nests of birds much smaller than itself, such as the dunnock and the European robin. A pair of small birds could hardly find enough food for a young cuckoo *and* their own offspring, but when these have been eliminated there is plenty for the cuckoo. In the case of those species of cuckoo that lay their eggs in the nests of birds as big or bigger than themselves, such as the great spotted cuckoo of southern Europe and

A young cuckoo being fed by its foster parent, a dunnock. Finding food for a single young cuckoo larger than themselves presents no more difficulties to the foster parents than would catering for their normal brood of four or five young dunnocks. The cuckoo, a parasite, has got rid of the foster parents' own young.

Africa, which lays in the nests of magpies, crows and large starlings, the young cuckoos do not eject their foster brothers, although it seems likely that their mother usually destroys one or more of her host's eggs when she lays her own.

However, although much is known about the common cuckoo and the American cowbirds, very little is known of the exact behavior of most other parasitic birds. If you are ever in any country where you could study some foreign cuckoo or one of the parasitic whydahs, you would probably be able to make a novel contribution to ornithological knowledge. For example, one of the commonest cuckoos in India, the koel, lays its eggs in the nests of the house crow. It is known that this crow attacks and drives away koels that come near its nest. Various theories have been put forward as to how the female koel may manage to enter the crow's nest and lay her egg without being harmed, but, so far as I know, nobody has actually proved how she does it. Cuckoos which lay in the nests of birds much smaller than themselves do not have this problem to the same degree, since the birds they impose upon could not inflict so much damage on them in the very short time, only a few seconds, which the hen cuckoo takes to lay one of her eggs. There is, however, little doubt that this speedy laying has developed as a means of avoiding injury by the hosts. It is also quite likely that in some species of birds (such as the warblers) particular fierceness towards the cuckoo has evolved as a means of protecting themselves from being parasitized. For example, they will usually attack a stuffed cuckoo with great fierceness if you place it anywhere near their nests. These birds will often forget all their fear of man and will perch on and peck at the eyes and head of a stuffed cuckoo while you are holding it in your hand. They do not, as used to be thought, mob the cuckoo because they mistake it for a sparrow hawk. If one holds a stuffed sparrow hawk in one's hand, the very same bird that, only a few seconds before, attacked the stuffed cuckoo fiercely will be frightened to come near it.

The lesser honey guide lays its eggs in the nests of barbets, a group of birds related to the woodpeckers, that make holes in trees to nest in. Its offspring gets rid of the rightful young of the barbets in a seemingly vicious way: when it is first hatched the young honey guide has sharp hooks on both its upper and lower mandibles (jaws). With these it repeatedly bites the soft bodies of the baby barbets until they die of their injuries.

Although the cuckoo takes no heed whatsoever of its young, beyond laying its eggs in a suitable nest, it seems possible that some other parasitic species do show some parental behavior. The African emerald cuckoo has been seen feeding a young bird of its own species after the latter had left its foster parents' nest. It is not known yet whether this is usual and whether, if so, each emerald cuckoo feeds its own young or merely any young emerald cuckoo of the right age that it comes across. The combassou is another parasitic species that seems capable of showing parental care in some circumstances. It is a little African weaver belonging to the same group as the other parasitic whydahs, although, unlike them, the male does not have a long tail when in his glossy black breeding plumage. In a wild state, it usually lays its eggs in the nest of the common fire finch, and has never been seen to build a nest for itself or to take any heed of its young. However, it is often kept in captivity and on at least two occasions captive combassous have nested, laid eggs and hatched their own young. This shows that at least some combassous still retain the instinct to build and incubate and may revert to this habit under certain circumstances. More usually, however, captive combassous either do not breed at all or else they lay their eggs in the nests of other birds kept with them. A wild female combassou that was watched laying her egg in West Africa made frequent visits to the fire finch's nest. From the way she dodged back it appeared that the incubating fire finch pecked at her when she did so, but in spite of this she finally went right into the nest with the fire finch, stayed there a few moments and then came out, having laid her egg. So far as is known, the combassou do not destroy the eggs or young of their hosts, since fire finches are often seen with a mixed brood of flying young. However, as the combassou is larger than the common fire finch, it is no doubt the young fire finches and not the young combassou in the same brood that suffer if there is any shortage of food.

Although birds that have helpless nestlings do not recognize their young as individuals until they leave the nest, many of them will notice quickly enough if there is an "odd" man among the brood. An egg or young one noticeably different from the rest will often be thrown out, or it may cause the birds to desert their nest. This behavior varies greatly between species, and probably it has only developed strongly in those which have long suffered from cuckoos or other parasitic birds. We find that the parasitic species show many similarities in their eggs or young to those of their hosts. The cuckoo, for example, usually lays eggs which are very much like those of the foster parent in color. From this we can be pretty sure that each hen cuckoo usually lays in the nest of the same kind of bird, almost certainly of the species that reared her when she was a nestling. The koel fledgling has a dark coloration, darker than that of the adult female koel, though not so black as the adult male koel, and a crow-like voice. The young combassou in its juvenile plumage is like a young common fire finch; it also has similar bright markings on the inside of its mouth. Such resemblances as these between the young of the parasite and those of its host have come about so that the foster parents would not reject or neglect the parasite's egg or young.

As always, we find some apparent ex-ceptions to the rule. In Britain, many cuckoos lay their eggs in the nest of the dunnock or hedge sparrow. When they do so they lay brownish, speckly eggs that are not in the least like the lovely deep blue eggs of the dunnock; yet the latter accepts and hatches the brown strange egg with its own. Here we can make a pretty likely guess that it is the dunnock's lack of discrimination which has made it unnecessary for the cuckoos para-sitizing them to lay eggs that would match. Possibly the dunnock is a species that has not been parasitized long enough for natural selection to have yet produced any change, either in its behavior towards strange eggs or in the egg color of its parasite. If, however, cuckoos continue to parasitize dunnocks, some few (and it need only be very few) dunnocks may begin to throw out the odd, brown egg then, as such dunnocks increase in population, we might expect to find dunnock-like cuckoo-eggs beginning to evolve.

The young of the common cuckoo is not much like the young of its foster parents. Indeed, once it has left the nest, both its appearance and its habit of sitting about on conspicuous perches are unlike those of a dunnock or any foster parent. Yet, as we know, the foster parents care for it just as devotedly as they would for their natural brood. Here, however, the parents have only had the one young one (for the young cuckoo threw out its foster brothers in the first few days of its life), they have had nothing else to compare it with and it has only by degrees grown to its large size and different ways. Furthermore, it seems pro-bable that the young cuckoo, with its piercing call and large, bright gape, supplies a supra-normal stimulus to the foster parents. To *their* way of looking at it, the young parasite is a "bigger and better" fledgling than one of their own would have been.

CHAPTER XVI

Preening, Bathing and Anting

IF YOU HAVE already watched birds, you will know that they spend much time preening their feathers. Often this is done at odd moments when they are resting and seem to have nothing better to do, but always after bathing or doing anything else that tends to disarrange or soil its plumage. When preening a feather the bird seizes it by the base and draws it through its bill, often making a nibbling or chewing movement as it does so. This serves to remove dirt from the feather and also to bring together and interlock any parts of the webbing that have become separated. It also may remove and swallow a film of preen oil that it had previously placed on the feather. Sunlight acting on this thinly spread oil forms vitamin D, and it is believed that birds can obtain all the vitamin D they need in this way. When anointing its body feathers, a bird may just run its oilcoated bill lightly over them without drawing individual feathers through the mandibles. You can often see domestic fowl do this when it starts to rain lightly. If the rain is heavy, they usually head for cover. The oil is secreted by the preen gland, which is just above the base of the tail (it is the "parson's nose" of your roast chicken), and to obtain it the bird seizes the gland in its bill and squeezes it to press out the oil, which then forms a thin film on the bill. To get oil onto the head feathers, birds scratch their bill with their feet and then scratch their head with their feet or rub their head on the preen gland or on parts of the plumage already oiled.

In some kinds of birds the preen gland does not appear to secrete any oil and is not used in preening. If you watch any pigeon preening, for example, you will see that it never seizes and squeezes its preening gland. In pigeons, and some other birds, a fine, whitish powdery substance, known as "powder-down" is produced by disintegration of certain small fluffy feathers and seems to serve instead of preen oil to keep the plumage in good condition. If you take a pigeon that is in good health and plumage, and hold it with its body pressed against your dark suit, you will find a white stain of powder-down on the cloth where it has been. Also, if you watch a healthy pigeon bathing, you will see that as soon as it goes into the water a film of powder-down forms around it on the surface.

While preening, birds also search for parasites and, if they can catch them, either eat them or cast them away. Many birds, such as pigeons, waxbills and other estrildine "finches" and some crows, indulge in mutual preening, in which two birds, usually mates, preen each other's heads. This preening of one bird by another is of great interest, because it has two quite different aspects, both of which are involved whenever it takes place. On what we might term a "practical" level the preening bird is helping the other to clean those parts of its body that it cannot reach with its own bill. Although birds can scratch their heads with their feet and rub them on branches or on their own shoulders, they cannot get rid of parasites so well in this way as with the bill. This is evident from the fact that one often finds birds with ticks on their heads, but hardly ever with ticks on other parts of their bodies.

The preening bird is also expressing its dominance over the other by preening it. The male and female of a mated pair often preen each other "turn and turn about," and then the mutual preening seems to be an expression of mutual affection. When the preening bird stops and offers its own head to its mate it is, in effect, relinquishing its mastery and offering to take the subordinate rôle. But if one individual always preens the other and never offers its own head for preening, then it is dominant and there is no sort of equality in the relationship between the two.

If you watch a number of mannikins and waxbills of different species in a crowded cage or aviary in a bird shop or a public zoo, you will notice that although, under these unnatural conditions, different kinds of birds will preen each other, smaller or weaker species do not preen larger or stronger species, though they often offer their own heads to them for preening. In such circumstances as these the aggressive element in the preening of another may be very evident, and sick or injured individuals may be preened so often and so roughly by their stronger fellow prisoners that their heads are plucked bare.

It does not follow, however, that a bird that lets itself be preened but never preens back is always being badly treated. On the contrary, at least among the waxbills and other estrildines, individuals sometimes seem to get much satisfaction at being preened by stronger birds. I once had two pairs of golden-breasted waxbills, a tiny African estrildine smaller than a wren, in an aviary with several blue waxbills, a somewhat larger and stronger species. Whenever the weaker of the two male golden-breasted waxbills had the worst of an encounter with his rival he would at once seek out one of the male blue waxbills and offer his head to him to be preened. Usually the blue waxbill was ready to oblige and both appeared to derive satisfaction from this arrangement. I must

Fig. 25. A female golden-breasted waxbill invites her mate to preen her head by erecting her head feathers.

add that neither of these two birds was "imprinted" on the other species and both had mates of their own kind at the time.

All water, marsh and sea birds bathe in water, as do many land birds also. The movements by which water is thrown up onto the plumage is similar in different groups of birds and you cannot do better than to watch a passerine bird (such as a starling or English sparrow), a pigeon, and a gull, to get a good idea of such small differences as there are in the bathing movements of different types of birds. Most passerines bathe hurriedly with continual movement, while pigeons and birds of prey wallow for half a minute or more between bouts of violent splashing. Some species, such as the robin, plunge quickly in and out of the water but do not stand in it and splash about as a starling or jay does. Some birds, such as the budgerigar and some other parrots, bathe by rubbing themselves on rain or dew-soaked leaves or grass. Pigeons bathe in rain showers by lying on one side and raising one wing to expose themselves to the falling rain, and they sometimes use this movement, quite inappropriately, when bathing in a pool or bird bath in dry weather.

Dust-bathing or dusting is shown chiefly by birds that are non aquatic and live on the ground, also by some arboreal species that live in dry, arid regions and get much of their food on the ground. The game birds, larks and bustards are dust-bathers, and the English sparrow is one of the few birds that bathes in both dust and water. Game birds,

135

as you will see if you watch a domestic fowl dusting itself, pull in the dust or fine soil towards them with a brisk hoe-like movement of the closed bill, scratch it up into the plumage with their feet and also throw it up with quick movements of their folded wings. They also lie on their sides and rub their heads and necks in the dust. English sparrows, on the other hand, use the same movements that they use in water bathing. The principal function of dusting seems to be that it helps to keep down the numbers of parasites on the birds, the fine dust blocking the breathing spiracles of lice and other insects, so that they die or become unwell, or at least some of them do, and so can be shaken out of the plumage when the bird shakes itself vigorously, as it always does after a dust bath. But there can be no doubt that the bird also gets a great deal of pleasure from dusting itself. If you have ever watched a farmyard chicken or a tame partridge dust-bathing, I think you will agree with me that this is one of the many good things of a bird's life that we deny to the wretched battery hens that supply most of our breakfast eggs. Both water bathing and dusting are instinctive. I once took a baby red-legged partridge that was only a few hours old and could hardly walk and placed it a few yards away from its nest. When the father bird, who was brooding the other young on the nest, called to it in answer to its "lost" cheeping, it tottered back to him. On the

way, however, it passed over some dusty soil. To my surprise it reacted at once to the feel of this dusty soil by squatting down and dust-bathing. It used all the movements that a grown bird would, including that of throwing up earth with its wings, although this movement is quite useless before the wing feathers have grown.

Sun-bathing is indulged in by most birds, perhaps all, including, rather surprisingly, many tropical species. Passerines sun-bathe in a characteristic posture, leaning to one side away from the sun with the body feathers erected and the near wing and near half of the tail spread. They usually open the bill and close or half-close the eye nearest the sun. Pigeons sun themselves in a similar posture, and both pigeons and passerines may, if the sun is almost directly above them, spread out both wings on either side in heraldic eagle style and fully spread the tail. Game birds lie on one side with the wings held a little away from the body and somewhat spread. They also squat down with their backs to the sun and the wings held loosely at the sides of the body, so that the back and rump are fully exposed to the sun's rays. This last posture seems to be the only one used by gulls and water fowl when sunbathing.

"Anting" is the term used for an astonishing pattern of behavior that is shown by many passerine birds. In it, the bird applies ants, usually worker ants of acid-secreting species,

Fig. 26. Some of the typical and surprising postures adopted when anting by chaffinch (left), jay (center) and song thrush (right).

A tame Baltimore oriole anting. It has just picked up an ant in its bill and has already brought one wing forward, supported by the forward depressed tail, in readiness to apply the ant to the primary wing feathers.

or other pungent substances, to its plumage, usually to the inner sides of its wing and tail quills. The anting bird picks up one or more ants in its bill, bends its head, partly opens and brings forward one or both wings and brushes the ant along the undersurface of the quills with a sharp downward stroke. The tail is also brought forward, often so far that the bird trips on it and falls over. Some species apply ants also to the tail and, less often, to other parts of the plumage. Some also lie down on the swarming ants with their wings spread. Some birds do not actually pick up ants in the bill when anting, although they make the movements of doing so. This is the case with the jay, which spreads and thrusts forward its wings so that the ants can swarm up into its plumage but does not pick up ants in its bill, or at any rate does not when using the wood ant, which is the species I have often seen it ant with. Besides other acid-secreting insects and pungent fruits some birds may use such unnatural objects as burning twigs or cigarette ends for anting. Possibly these things may supply a supra-normal stimulus in some cases.

The function of anting is unknown. It is possible that the formic acid may have some beneficial effect on the plumage or a harmful effect on parasites. One respect, however, in which anting differs from water- or dust-bathing is that whereas all birds that dust- or water-bathe do so frequently, individual birds, of species known to ant, may not do so at all. On the other hand they may do so quite often, or only very occasionally. Anting is one of the many aspects of bird behavior about which much yet remains to be discovered.

It is difficult to see anting often under natural conditions, although you will sooner or later have the luck to do so if you keep a sharp watch out for it. You can, however, be fairly certain of seeing anting if you collect a sackful of wood ants one summer day and tip them out onto a lawn or near a bird feeder where many wild birds regularly come to feed. Then watch from a window or other hidden point of vantage. If many starlings visit the place while the ants are still present in numbers above ground, you are almost certain to see some of them ant.

Birds clean their bills by wiping or scraping them on some solid object, usually their perch, and by scratching them with their feet. You must have seen an English sparrow or canary "sharpening its bill," as the action is popularly but incorrectly termed. These two species, like other passerines, scrape the bill first on one side of the branch, or whatever else they are perched on, and then on the other with a movement suggestive of a man stropping a razor. Most aquatic birds clean their bills by dipping them in the water and shaking them. Pigeons, whose bills are soft at the base and easily injured, never scrape or rub their bills on anything, but only clean them by scratching the bill, especially at the corner of the mouth, with one foot. Many kinds of birds show the bill-cleaning movements also as displacement-movements (see page 101).

CHAPTER XVII

Roosting

Most birds go to roost at night, that is, they retire to some particular place in the evening and remain there, sleeping or resting, until the following morning. There are many exceptions to this general rule, but it holds good for the majority. Most diurnal birds can see little or not at all by night and they do not leave their roosting place during the hours of darkness unless they are forced to do so. On the other hand most nocturnal or crepuscular birds, such as nightjars, most owls and the woodcock, which roost by day, can see quite well in daylight.

A good roosting place must therefore offer its user safety, or at least relative safety, from attack by predators and sufficient shelter to maintain it in health. The problem of finding such a roosting place is solved in different ways by different kinds of birds.

Many birds roost socially, not only species that habitually associate in flocks by day, but also many that do not. The impulse that prompts the individual birds to gather to roost is probably connected with feelings of apprehension or insecurity caused by the gathering darkness, but since the habit is so widespread it is fairly certain that it must have survival value. In fact, each individual in a large roosting flock not only, in all probability, feels safer in company but actually is safer than it would be if it were roosting alone. It is less easy to see why this should be so, since it might seem that a crowd of birds all flying to and roosting in one place would be likely to attract the attention of predators. Perhaps, however, the difficulties a predator would have in catching any particular individual before some other had been disturbed and given the alarm, more than compensates for this. On the other hand, the advantages of social roosting, at least in some cases, may not be the question of safety at night. It might, for example, be useful if it serves to enable unrelated birds to meet and get to know one another.

Many communal roosts are traditional, but new ones are sometimes formed and old ones deserted, usually without anyone being aware of the reasons. If you are ever able to watch and record the forming of a new communal roost or the abandonment of a traditional one (not, of course, the mere temporary desertion of a winter roost by the breeding population), your observations would certainly contribute towards a better understanding of the species concerned and the functions of the communal roost in its life.

Social roosting is generally found in birds that roost in places where there is plenty of room for all the individuals of even large flocks, as is the case with birds that roost in the branches of trees, in reed beds or on the ground in open fields. With species that roost in sites, such as holes or crevices, that are usually in short supply, matters are different.

Not only does each woodpecker retire at night to its own roosting hole but the chickadees that have formed a loose flock to feed during the winter day separate in the evening, each roosting alone in some small hole or niche that it has found and claimed for itself.

Some birds, such as crows, which usually roost high in the bare branches of large trees, seem to care nothing for shelter when roosting. Most birds, however, appear to seek some degree of protection from the elements. For example, the winter roosts of sparrows and finches are usually in thick evergreens and those of mourning doves preferably in conifers or else among low, densely growing trees on islands. Similarly, if you observe the roosting starlings and feral pigeons on buildings in towns you will see how those ledges best sheltered from wind and rain are most favored by them. In all these cases, however, it is probable that safety as well as comfort has been a factor influencing the choice of relatively sheltered roosting places, since birds in thick cover or on overhung ledges are less likely to be seen easily by owls or other nocturnal predators.

Some kinds of birds cluster together in contact with one another at night. In these species it is evident that the advantages of increased comfort and protection from cold have been greater than the added safety of maintaining individual distance when roosting. This clustering is done by many small birds that live in hot climates, and is probably connected with the relatively greater drop in temperature at night in the tropics and sub tropics. The bronze-winged mannikin, a small seed-eating estrildine "finch" from Africa, actually makes communal nests each night for roosting purposes, though these roosting nests built by non-breeding individuals are rough-and-ready affairs when compared with the breeding nest. Some birds, like the wren, usually roost in company in cold weather but not at other times.

One should remember that a bird forced to leave its roost after dark is in danger of being caught by an owl or of injuring itself against obstacles as it flies blindly in the dark. Even being forced to leave a sheltered roosting place and spend the rest of the night in a more exposed place might mean death to an ill-nourished small bird in winter. If, therefore, one really needs to look at a roosting bird after dark for any reason, it will be best to go just before dawn, when if disturbed the bird will only have a little while to wait till daylight.

Section 3

CHAPTER XVIII

Migration

MIGRATION IS OFTEN thought to be confined to birds, but actually many other kinds of animals, such as butterflies, fish, and mammals make regular seasonal migrations. Typical migratory movements of birds are easy to observe. One day there are robins on the lawn and the next day, when the weather starts to turn cool, they are gone; in the same way, early in spring, they reappear from one day to the next, bustling about looking for earthworms in the garden and acting as if they had never left.

In spring and autumn we can see flocks of birds on migration, dropping from the skies to feed and rest for the night. Larger birds, such as Canada geese can be seen flying in V-formation, and at night we can hear the voices of smaller birds as they pass overhead. Graber and Cochran at Champaign, Illinois, by recording the call notes of birds passing overhead, mostly olive-backed thrush, gray-cheeked thrush and veery, estimate a density of 78,800 calls in May and 294,000 calls in September.

Much has been learned about the actual course of migration from scientific studies such as these. We have come a long way from the ancient belief that swallows spend the winter hibernating in the mud at the bottom

of lakes or ponds. In fact, a recent discovery showed that at least one species of birds, the poor-will, actually does hibernate.

There are three methods of studying migration. One is by direct observation of birds, such as done by Graber and Cochran (just cited), or Lowery, who observed birds as they became visible in passing across the disc of the moon. To this category has been added recently the observation of birds by means of radar echoes. A second method is the tracing of the movements of individual birds. Bird-banding has grown into a huge international venture and, in spite of the relatively low rates of return, much has been accomplished by this means. Finally, there are experimental approaches, which will be treated more fully in the next chapter.

Why do birds migrate?

We know that it cannot be merely the lack of food which starts the migrants on their way. Many birds migrate long before their food supply runs low and go much further than their need to find new feeding grounds would dictate. This explanation also would leave open the question of why birds return in the spring, often before the weather is warm enough to assure a good food supply.

Many birds do not undertake any long-range migration, of course. Some species are only partially migratory, the robin, for example; also in the starling we find both migratory and nonmigratory individuals side by side. In general, the more northern the habitat the greater the tendency to migrate; seed-eaters are more likely to spend the winter in their breeding range than to move south. Even in many of the sedentary species we find that there is considerable lateral or even northerly movement in the young birds, after they have learned to take care of themselves.

In the starling it has been shown, for example, that from their point of introduction and release in Central Park in New York City in 1890, their westward movement was mainly carried out by the young birds. They fanned out after they had matured sufficiently, and started to band together in the fall. In this manner the starling has within half a century reached as far west as Alaska and as far south as Guatemala.

The reason why birds migrate is now well on its way to a solution. Much of the credit for this accomplishment is due to the observations of a Canadian biologist, William Rowan, who first discovered the relationships which were the basis of the migratory urge. It was well known that birds of a given locality tended to return to their nesting areas on practically the same days each year. Just think of the swallows of Capistrano! Since weather, food supply and temperature were much too variable to provide such precise timing, the reason had to be sought in some unchanging physical phenomenon. The only factor which was capable of providing a fixed date was one based on the same cause which provided the seasons themselves: the course of the earth around the sun. Testing his hypothesis he found that providing increasing lengths of light each day would bring the birds into migratory condition long before their normal time.

Thereafter the pieces of the puzzle started to fall into place. It was already known that increased length of light would affect the breeding condition of birds. The action of the lengthening days would bring about a growth of the gonads (see Chapter XIX). This phenomenon in turn would be the cause of the birds starting to migrate. Dr. Rowan then tested his theory by artificially lengthening the day for some slate-colored juncos by supplying them with extra light. Examination showed that their reproductive system was in the state of growth normally found in spring. When he released these birds they migrated northward.

These experiments pointed the way, but still left many unanswered questions. What about equatorial and transequatorial migrants, which would spend their days in equal or even shortening lengths of daylight in the spring? Today we know that it is not only the length of day, but particularly the lengthening of darkness in the fall, which seems to initiate the annual cycle. We know the deposition of fat, a good preparation for long flights, plays a rôle as important as that of the gonads, and that hormones secreted by the pituitary gland control the sexual cycle. So the why of migration seems well on its way to a solution.

Where do birds migrate?

In general we think of migration as running north-south and vice versa. This is not really quite correct, but will serve as a convenient generalization. Perhaps it would be better to say that birds fly from colder climates to more temperate zones. For example, Great Britain gets many winter visitors, which are escaping the colder weather of the European continent. There even exists what is called "vertical migration," where birds migrate between different levels in mountainous areas.

We can distinguish resident birds, such as the English sparrow, which moves about within its range, but never leaves it entirely. Then we have birds with an overlapping range, such as the starling, with the more northern birds coming south to join their resident brethren; or the robin, with the Canadian birds coming down to the Middle Atlantic states, while the residents of these

Many birds, such as some gulls and some plovers, that migrate or move from place to place in flocks, tend to fly in a V-shaped formation. This tendency is particularly marked in geese and is well shown in this photograph of a flock of Canada geese in flight.

regions are away at the Gulf Coast. Still others, such as the fox sparrow or the yellow-throat seem to leapfrog, with the more northerly birds flying over the home territory of the more favorably situated birds to winter further south. Finally there are migrants in which summer range and wintering grounds are clearly separated. Often we find a widely dispersed summer range and a clearly defined wintering ground. As examples, we might take the pine warbler, rock wren, field sparrow, loggerhead shrike, or the rose-breasted grosbeak.

Most Canadian birds winter in the U.S., birds of the northern U.S. fly to the Gulf, while many birds of the central U.S. fly to the West Indies, Central and South America. Some species travel much longer distances to winter in the southern hemisphere. A well known example is the barn swallow, which winters as far south as Argentina. Another such bird is the bobolink, which has recently been studied extensively (see Chapter XIX). The long-distance champions are the shore birds and the sea birds, such as the Pacific golden plover which regularly mi-

grates between Alaska and Hawaii. The Arctic tern summers above the Arctic Circle and winters in the Antarctic, making the 22,000-mile journey twice each year.

Migration paths seem to be dictated by topographical features; they follow mainly the great river valleys and lead around mountainous regions. In the U.S., four great flyways can be distinguished: 1) The Atlantic flyway is traveled up and down the coast and then either across the Gulf of Mexico or skirting it via Florida and the chain of the West Indies; 2) The Mississippi flyway is probably the heaviest traveled route, from the Great Lakes up and down the Mississippi Valley and then either across the Gulf or down the spine of the continent across Mexico and into Central America; 3) the Central flyway, starting at the Mackenzie River and down the Great Plains, and finally, 4) on the West Coast, birds will follow the shore line or take the oceanic route from Alaska to California then to Mexico and beyond.

In other parts of the world local features distort the main north-south flow of migration. British birds travel mainly to France, Spain, Portugal and then into Africa, but many continental European birds show a distinct southwesterly or southeasterly trend. Danish storks travel south to the Balkans and then on to Egypt, while West German and Dutch birds take a southwesterly route. Europe itself serves as wintering quarters for birds from Greenland, Scandinavia and northern Asia. Some Asian birds travel to India and Ceylon, while others take a route that lands them in Malaya and Indonesia. Some birds, however, have been known actually to cross the Himalayas. Migration in the southern hemisphere is not as extensive. Still there are South African birds which travel north during the southern winter. Some Australian and New Zealand species travel to winter quarters located in the Polynesian islands, the Solomons and the Bismarck Islands; among such migrants are, for instance, the long-tailed cuckoo and the bronze cuckoo.

How do birds migrate?

How birds get from their breeding grounds to their winter quarters has long been of interest to the student of bird behavior. There are some answers to many of the obvious questions, but it generally is also true that these observations admit many exceptions.

A good deal of migration goes on at night. The smaller songbirds especially tend to be nocturnal migrants, even though they live their normal life by day. The reason for this is thought to be the constant need for food to replace the energy used up in flying. Another is the relative safety from predators which flying by night affords. Yet nocturnal migration does harbor a peculiar danger for birds. This is the danger of flying into ob-

stacles such as lighthouses, television towers and tall buildings like the Empire State building in New York. Why these accidents occur is still a puzzle. But it does give us a clue to the species of birds which migrate at night and throws some light on the height at which migrating birds fly.

Eugene Odum of the University of Georgia collected birds killed at a tower and measured the fat content of their bodies. He found three patterns. One kind, the Savannah sparrow, for example, begins its short-range migration before any extra fat is deposited. A second kind becomes moderately obese before beginning migration. This type is represented by the white-throated sparrow and the white-crowned sparrow. A third type becomes extremely fat just before migration. To this group belong the long-range migrants, which typically breed in the U.S. but winter in South America and are obliged to cross the Gulf of Mexico. A scarlet tanager had 51 per cent of its body weight made up of fat, whereas in the ruby-throated hummingbird the dry weight of fat may be up to three-and-a-half times more than the dry weight of all other tissues of the premigratory bird. Translating the energy content which this fat represents into flight range shows that these tiny humming-birds are not only capable of crossing the Gulf nonstop, but that they accumulate enough fuel to start out from several hundred miles inland.

Most of the birds which migrate by day are larger and sturdier than those which migrate at night. We also find that they tend to be good fliers, like the swallows, which not only can evade predators by superior flying, but also are able to catch insects on the wing. The following table summarizes our knowledge of the kinds of birds which migrate by day or by night, listed in the standard order of classification:

Some Night Migrants

Rails	Flycatchers	Kinglets	Bobolink
Cuckoos	(short-tailed)	Hummingbirds	Orioles
Whip-poor-wills	Wrens	Vireos	Tanagers
Woodpeckers	Thrushes	Warblers	Grosbeaks
	Sparrows (native)	Buntings	

Some Day Migrants

Loons	Doves	Chickadees	Blackbirds
Pelicans	Nighthawks	Crows	Cowbirds
Storks	Swifts	Robins	Purple finches
Vultures	Flycatchers	Bluebirds	Grosbeaks (boreal)
Hawks	(long-tailed)	Pipits	Redpolls
Grouse	Kingbirds	Waxwings	Goldfinches
Cranes	Swallows	Shrikes	Siskins
Gulls	Longspurs	Starlings	Crossbills

Some Migrants, Either Day or Night

Herons	Egrets	Shorebirds	Geese
		Ducks	

(Table after Leonard W. Wing, *Natural History of Birds*, New York, Ronald Press, 1956)

Once on migration, birds tend to travel quite leisurely, stopping now and then to feed and rest. The return in spring is normally accomplished much faster than the corresponding trip in fall. It is as if the nest and unborn young were calling on the birds to hurry up and get home. Generally migrants fly low, keeping below 3,000 ft. Over water, birds tend to travel at lower levels than over land, typically flying at 10 to 100 feet above water. Some recent radar data indicate, however, that an unseen migration may also go on at higher levels, especially if there is an overcast.

CHAPTER XIX

Orientation, Navigation and Homing

EVEN IF WE KNOW why birds migrate, where they fly, and how they get there, a most intriguing problem remains: how does the bird know where it must go and how does it determine its position? We can distinguish three related problems: 1) *Orientation*—how the bird establishes its own position and thus gets to know where it is. All birds seem to be capable of making this judgment to some extent, at least in their home territory. 2) *Navigation*—how the bird is able to take off in a given direction, keep its course during flight and finally recognize its goal when it gets there. Migrating birds must be able to make such decisions. 3) *Homing*—some birds if carried to unfamiliar territory and then released, can return to their nest or loft. This means that they must be able to judge the home direction from any place, in addition to all abilities needed for migration. The most familiar example of a bird that can do this is the homing pigeon. Other birds that have been tested and found to have good homing ability are starlings, herring gulls, Leach's petrel, Manx shearwater and Laysan albatross.

Incidentally, pigeons are not the only birds that have been used for carrying messages. It is said that in the Pacific natives have long used trained frigate birds for communication between islands.

Field studies

One way in which a bird becomes familiar with its surroundings has often been observed by fanciers of homing pigeons. The young bird, when first ready to fly, will perch on a nearby tree or building and survey its environment. It sticks pretty close to home for the first few days, circling around with the other pigeons of the flock and becoming more and more familiar with the surroundings of the loft. Particular landmarks in the vicinity seem to be used as an aid to orientation. If the pigeon is 'to be trained for homing, the owner eventually takes it further and further away, until it has become familiar with a route.

It seems pretty clear that orientation is established gradually by learning the main features of the environment in a series of exploratory flights. If the bird is taken out of the known area it will search for known territory by circling. Airplane observations have confirmed that a more or less spiral search pattern is the usual mode employed.

Orientation has been tested on many different species of birds. Usually this has been done by taking birds some distance from their home grounds and releasing them. One odd feature of these experiments has been the fact that even when the distances involved were quite short (less than 25 miles) many of the birds failed to return. A reason for this apparent lack of orientation may be the lack of motivation to return, when releases took place outside the breeding season. Somewhat better results are achieved when nests or young provide an incentive for the birds to return home. Pigeon fanciers know this trick quite well, and make use of it in pigeon races.

On the other hand, even inexperienced birds have sometimes returned over long distances. The instances when birds oriented successfully are just as puzzling as the failure of many birds to come back over short distances. In 1947 Yeagly released some pigeons in Pennsylvania, which had been trained originally in Nebraska, to test a theory that certain conditions relating to the earth's magnetism were identical in both places, and would cause his birds to fly off in a direction parallel to the original training direction. The experiment was unsuccessful, but three birds returned all the way to Nebraska over completely strange country. G. V. T. Matthews in England reports on an experiment in which a Manx shearwater was flown from its home in Wales to Boston, a distance of 3,000 miles. This bird, which could not possibly have had any experience in flying across the Atlantic, returned to its nest in 12 days, beating the news of its release which had been sent regular mail, by a matter of 10 hours!

The long distance champion is a Laysan albatross, which took part in an experiment conducted by Kenyon and Rice in 1957. Eighteen albatrosses, sitting on eggs or with newly hatched young, were caught on Midway Island and flown by airplane to six different points all around the Pacific. (Each bird's partner took good care of the young during the experiment.) Fourteen birds returned to their nests, including some from each of the release points in the Marshall Islands, Marianas, Philippines, Japan, Hawaii and the state of Washington. The longest distance covered was 4,120 statute miles from Sangley Point, near Manila, in the Philippines. This particular bird took 32 days to home. The fastest flight was accomplished by an albatross released on Whidby Island, Washington, which flew 3,200 miles in about 10 days, an average speed of 320 miles per day.

Following birds by means of an airplane could establish the route which birds take in returning to their home and would help us to understand how they orient themselves. However, this is a very expensive procedure; and besides, it is not easy to follow a single bird visually from a plane. Apart from these drawbacks the airplane might disturb the bird by coming too close. A promising new technique in tracing birds, telemetry, just coming into use, is to strap a small radio transmitter on a bird's back and follow the radio signals emitted.

Another method that has been used has led to some odd results. This technique establishes the direction in which a bird vanishes when released. The experimenter follows the bird with binoculars until it is out of sight and records in which compass direction it had been flying when last seen. In many releases the vanishing direction agrees well with the home direction. But in some experiments on mallard ducks carried out by Matthews in England and by Bellrose in Illinois, the ducks were oriented all right, as shown by the constancy of the vanishing points, only they all flew north, regardless of the true home direction.

These experiments show that at least some birds are quite capable of orienting themselves and homing, even over long distances and unfamiliar territories. How about birds on migration? We might credit the experienced migrant with a good enough memory to remember the route flown in the fall and to retrace his flight on the way north, but this feat is highly unlikely. Tests of their memory indicate that they can indeed remember places over long periods of time, but it takes them much longer than just one experience to learn about the landmarks which must guide them. In addition, there are many birds which return by a different route from the one they traveled on their way to the winter quarters. Also, of course, there are no landmarks over the ocean and many birds cross large bodies of water, such as the Gulf of Mexico or the Mediterranean or even wide stretches of the Pacific. Finally, and most remarkable of all, young birds on their first trip often travel by themselves or are capable of doing so.

Experiments made on storks, starlings, hooded crows, American crows and sparrow hawks by different investigators prove that young birds released after the usual migration of the adult stock will still fly to the usual wintering grounds and return the next spring. Young birds displaced east or west have been found to travel a course parallel to the usual migration route. Interestingly enough, when these birds returned the next spring they came back to the area where they had been taken for release and not to the area where they were hatched. Older and more experienced birds compensate for the displacement and fly to their normal range. For example, Perdeck transported some 11,000 starlings caught in autumn from their wintering grounds in Holland and released them in Switzerland. These birds originated in Scandinavia, the Baltic countries, Poland, northern Germany and Holland. After displacement, the adults aimed northwest, back to their normal winter area, but the juveniles aimed southwest and flew to southern France, Spain and Portugal. Recoveries of ringed birds in later years showed that the adults had come back to Holland, but the juveniles tended to return to the wintering area reached after their displacement. How birds know the right direction to take is still one of the great unsolved puzzles of nature.

Laboratory studies

The most startling discovery that has been made about birds has been their ability to orient to the sun and the stars. This ability, if precise enough, could form the basis of a system of celestial navigation like that used by the sailor at sea or the pilot or navigator in the air.

Although the idea that the sun could act as a compass had occurred before, and the use of a sun-compass had been demonstrated in bees and other insects, it remained for a German ornithologist, Gustav Kramer, to prove conclusively in 1950 that birds could use the sun for direction-finding. There are two types of experiments. One is based on the fact that birds will flutter about in a preferred direction when caged during their normal period of migration. This so-called migratory restlessness was exhibited in a circular cage from which only the sky was visible. A starling was placed in the cage and an observer estimated the direction taken by the bird, by crawling underneath the cage and looking up through the glass bottom to record its position. The other type of experiment also used starlings. This time the starlings were trained to a particular compass direction and showed their ability by going to one of 12 food containers, prying it open with their beaks and getting a bit of food. The cage and containers were rotated to make sure that it was the direction and not the particular container that was chosen. When the sky was overcast the starlings chose at random. If mirrors were used to reflect the sun from a new direction the starlings were fooled and changed their choices accordingly. Even an artificial sun, made up of a 250-watt light bulb shining through a cheesecloth could be used to train the birds successfully.

This use of the sun as a compass depends on the bird's ability to judge how the sun moves across the sky. The bird also needs a good sense of time, so that the sun's position can be compared with the time of day, to provide it with a clue to the direction. At noon, for example, a bird would know that south is directly in the direction of the sun, or if it wanted to fly east, it would have to keep the sun at its right. Of course, a bird would have to adjust its path continuously to compensate for the apparent movement of the sun.

The reality of this time sense has been proven in experiments in which starlings were kept on an artificial day, 6 hours different from the normal. When tested under the real sun they made their choices with an error of about the expected amount and direction. Pigeons which were released after a similar shift flew off at right angles to their home direction.

If the sun's position in relation to time is used for orientation during the day, what about nighttime? Experiments on birds which normally migrate at night showed that the stars provide the same kind of cues as the sun does during the day. Even when tested under the artificial sky of a planetarium, oriented migratory restlessness was found. Another experiment demonstrated not only that bobolinks could orient by the stars, but also that they showed their normal regional differences. Birds from North Dakota and birds from a different group in New York could be distinguished by the direction of their fluttering, just like their normal relative course would demand.

These experiments have shown how birds can fly in a given direction, navigating with the help of the sun or the stars. But they do not explain how a bird, displaced from home, can find out how to get back to its nest. What is needed is a grid, something like our lines of longitude and latitude. Magnetic lines of force have been proposed, but had to be rejected. The same happened to all attempts based on other factors which birds could not detect. One proposed theory utilized the height of the sun's arc across the sky, another the rate at which the sun changed its altitude. Still another tried to base itself on the apparent position of the stars. None of them have proved satisfactory.

What, then, is the emerging picture of our present state of knowledge? Birds can use the sun and the stars to hold to a given direction, in other words, as a compass to guide them in their flights. What we do not know is how they find the direction in which to fly. Knowledge of landmarks and such guide lines as river valleys and mountain chains undoubtedly plays a large rôle. Search for known surroundings seems to play a part too. But much of the mystery remains. We still do not know how young and inexperienced birds know the direction in which to migrate, nor how older birds home from completely strange territory. We still find it hard to explain the flights of migrating birds on overcast days; we know though, that migrants favor clear weather for take-off. These facts, which do not readily fit in with anything we know, suggest there is still an undiscovered factor which plays a rôle in bird navigation.

INDEX

Merganser (*Mergus merganser*), *53*, 55
Migration, 21, 25, 140–144, 145, 147
Mimicry, 98
Moa (*Dinornithidae*), 39
Mobbing, 90, 91, 93, 95
Molt, 47–49, 92
Moorhen, see Gallinule
Mortality, 18, 20
Murre (*Uria aalge*): adaptations, 32; appearance, 23; eggs, 11, 13, 14; habitat, 29
Murre, Brünnich's or northern (*Uria lomvia*), 34
Muscles, 62

Navigation, 145
Nestlings, 18, 34, 47, 104, 105, 108, 121, 128
Nests: building, 72, 116, 118; cliffs, 34, *110*, 111; colonial, 10, 107, 109–111; ground, 11, 116, 130; in holes, 104, 107, 113, 118, 129; parasitizing, 11, 13, 131; relief, 73; sites, 7, 8, 34, 107, 116–121
Nest-shaping movements, 118
Nighthawk (*Chordeiles minor*), 80, 104, 144
Nightingale (*Luscinia megarhynchos*), 50
Nightjar (*Caprimulgus europaeens*—Europe, *Caprimulgus vociferus*—America), 25, 104, 138
Nocturnal habits, 9, 30, 104, 138, 143
Notornis, see Takahe
Number of birds, by kinds, 37; by species, 26, 32
Nutcracker (*Nucifraga caryocatactes*—Europe), 18, 87
Nuthatch (*Sitta carolininensis*): color, 35; feeding habits, 18, 30, 87

Oceans, 30–32
Orientation, 145–147
Oriole, Baltimore (*Icterus galbula*), 116, 137
Oropendola, olive, 172
Osprey (*Pandion haliaetus*), 24, 85
Ostrich (*Struthio camelus*): escaping, 36; flight modifications, 37; gizzard, 56; young, 121
Ovenbirds (*Furnasidae*), 26
Owl, barn (*Tyto alba*), 22
Owl, boobook (*Ninox boobook*—Australia), 129
Owl, fish (*Scotopelia sp.*—Africa, *Ketupa sp.*—Asia), 85
Owl, long-eared (*Asio-otus*), 67
Owl, tawny (*Strix aluco*), 93
Owls (*Strigidae*): as predators, 19, 90; cryptic color, 104; egg color, 11; eye, 66; fear, recognition of, 93; feeding, 85, 129; nesting, 117; nestlings, 128; relationship, 83; roosting, 138; sight, 64
Owls, short-eared (*Asio flammeus*), 67
Oxygen supply, 41, 59
Oyster catcher (*Haematopus palliatus*—America, *Haematopus ostralegus*—Europe): bill, 33; eggs, 11; range, 22; stimuli, 76; young, 123

Pair formation, 112
Parakeet, Bourke's (*Neopsephotus bourkei*), 103
Parakeet, grass (*Neophema sp.*), 103
Parasitizing, 11, 13, 75, 131, 132, 133
Parental care, 11, 14, 18, 31, 36, 47, 105, 121–131
Parrot, gray (*Psittacus erithacus*), 74
Parrots (*Psittacidae*): faunal regions, 26; food, 81; foot modifications, 35; mimicry, 98; nesting in holes, 104
Partridge, chukkar or red-legged (*Alectoris rufa*), 74, 121
Partridge, Hungarian or European gray (*Perdix perdix*), 25, 36
Passerines or song birds: bathing, 135; coloration, 50; language, 98; song, 20, 104
Peacock (*Pavo cristatus*), 99, 101
Pelicans (*Pelecanidae*), 37, 144
Pellets, 57, 88
Penguin, emperor (*Aptenodytes forsteri*), 30, 120
Penguin, fairy (*Eudyptula minor*), 29
Penguin, gentoo (*Pygoscelis papua*), 28
Penguin, king (*Aptenodytes patagonica*), 30, 120

Penguin, little, see Penguin, fairy
Penguins (*Spheniscidae*), 27, 32, 37
Petrel, storm (*Hydrobates pelagicus*), 30
Petrels (*Procellariidae*): adaptation to environment, 30; beak, 53; colonization changes, 20; incubation period, 15; nestlings, 128
Phalarope, northern (*Lobipes lobatus*), 14
Phalaropes (*Phalaropodidae*), 14, 26
Pheasant, Argus (*Argusianus argus*), 104, 105, 123
Pheasant, golden (*Chrysolophus pictus*), 75
Pheasants (*Phasianidae*): eggs, 10, 11; faunal regions, 25; feeding habits, 83, 88; habitat, 36; hearing, 67; importation of, 20
Phoebe, eastern (*Sayornis phoebe*), 52
Pigeon, domestic, feral or rock (*Columba livia*): display, 108, *115*; driving, 109; pairing, 113; recognition of predators, 92
Pigeon, wood (*Columba palumbus*), 25
Pigeons (*Columbidae*): bathing, 135; courtship displays, 99; driving, 109; egg color, 11; feeding, 88, 128; food canal, 57; incubating, 73; muscles, 62; nests, 116; preening, 134; young, 48, 105
Pigeons, homing, 145
Pigments, 50
Pipits (*Motacillidae*), 13, 144
Playing with fire, 94
Plover, golden (*Pluvialis dominica*), 48, 76, 142
Plover, ringed (*Charadrius hiaticula*): eggs, 11, 13; coloration, 103; reactions to man, 94
Plovers (*Charadriidae*), 49
Plumage, sequence of, 48
Plumules, 46
Pneumatic bones, 59
Pochard, red-crested (*Netta rufina*), 123
Pochard, rosy-billed (*Metopiana peposaca*), 123
Poor-will (*Phalaenoptilus nuttalli*), 140
Population: and food supply, 18; annual fluctuations, 16–18; conservation, 19; control, 18, 20; dispersal, 20, 23, 24
Powder-down, 47, 134
Prairie chicken (*Tympanuchus cupido*), 36
Predators: danger from, 89–91, 111; protection against, 11, 14, 31, 36, 102, 103, 105, 116; recognition of, 91–93
Preening, 45, 94, 101, 134
Ptarmigan, rock (*Lagopus mutus*), 11, 36
Ptarmigan, willow (*Lagopus lagopus*), 69
Puffin (*Fratercula arctica*), 29, 34
Puffin, horned (*Fratercula corniculata*), *54*, 86
Pyriform eggs, 13

Quail, see Bobwhite

Races, geographical, 69
Rails (*Rallidae*), 33, 124, 144
Range: defining, 31; overlapping, 141; size of, 21
Raven (*Corvus corax*), 34
Re-directed aggression, 109
Redpoll, Hornemann's (*Acanthis hornemanni*), 69
Redpoll, lesser (*Acanthis flammea*), 50, 69
Redpoll, mealy (*Acanthis flammea*), 69
Redstart (*Setophaga ruticilla*—America, *Phoenicurus phoenicurus*—Europe), 50, 70, 118
Reproductive organs, 10, 65, 141
Robbing, 86, 87, 91, 107, 118
Robin (*Turdus migratorius*—American): breeding territory, 107; color, 104; eggs, 13; feeding habits, 79; migration, 141, 144; nests, 116, 119; plumage, 49; variations, 70
Robin (*Erithacus rubecula*—European): color, 70; feeding habits, 78; rearing cuckoos, 131
Rooks (*Corvus frugilegus*): breeding territory, 107; burying food, 88; mates, 112; nest building, 117
Roosting, 138

Sandpiper, purple (*Erolia maritima*), 96
Sandpiper, spotted (*Actitus macularia*), 13
Sandpipers (*Scolopacidae*), 33
Scaup, lesser (*Aythya affinis*), 19
Scoter, velvet (*Melanitta deglandi*), 20